LAB MANUAL

Glencoe Science
Pre-AP Series

Biology
Pre-AP

Mc
Graw
Hill

New York, New York   Columbus, Ohio   Chicago, Illinois   Peoria, Illinois   woodland Hills, California

GLENCOE SCIENCE PRE-AP SERIES
Biology Pre-AP Lab Manual

 Glencoe

The *McGraw-Hill* Companies

Send all inquiries to:
Glencoe/McGraw-Hill
8787 Orion Place
Columbus, OH 43240-4027

ISBN 0-07-869867-7

Printed in the United States of America.

7 8 9 10   079   12 11 10 09

Contents

To the Teacher

This Pre-AP Biology Lab Manual contains 17 laboratory activities that are designed for a high school Pre-AP biology curriculum. Each activity is based on the AP recommended lab topics.

Pre-AP instructional strategies are built into each lab to help you build a successful Pre-AP course. Students are encouraged to draw inferences, to ask questions using six levels of questioning (knowledge recall, comprehension, application, analysis, synthesis, and evaluation), to implement the yes-but strategy for analyzing an argument, and to synthesize perspectives from different points of view.

Each lab begins with background information for each activity. In the Objectives, there is a description of the purpose of each activity. Under Materials, you are provided with the reagents, equipment, and supplies needed in the activity. Instructions for completing the lab emphasize developing student skills in carefully following directions and in observing, measuring, and recording data in an organized manner. The Data and Analysis section includes tables and space for students to record their data and observations. Additionally, major concepts and objectives are drawn together in this section. Students are required to answer questions that require analysis of experimental data.

The Teacher Edition provides a variety of helpful information about each activity in the form of a Teacher Guide section. Teaching tips, helpful comments and suggestions, objectives, and time allotments, as well as answers to all questions, are to be found in this section.

Correlation to Glencoe Biology Programs

The activities in Glencoe's *Biology Pre-AP Lab Manual* coordinate with the following chapters in these Glencoe biology programs. Use this chart to help plan the best way to use these activities with your classes.

	Glencoe Biology	Biology: The Dynamics of Life	BSCS Biology: A Molecular Approach	Biology: An Everyday Experience	Biology: Living Systems
Measuring Diffusion Rates	Chapter 7	Chapter 6, Chapter 8	Chapter 3	Chapter 2	Chapter 4
Normal and Plasmolyzed Cells	Chapter 7	Chapter 8	Chapter 3	Chapter 2	Chapter 4
Extracellular Enzymes	Chapter 6	Chapter 6	Chapter 2	Chapter 10	Chapter 3
How does the environment affect mitosis?	Chapter 9	Chapter 8	Chapter 8, Chapter 10	Chapter 22	Chapter 7
Observation of Meiosis	Chapter 10	Chapter 10	Chapter 12	Chapter 22	Chapter 7
Influencing the Rate of Photosynthesis	Chapter 8	Chapter 9	Chapter 4	Chapter 6, Chapter 19	Chapter 6
Chloroplast Pigment Analysis	Chapter 8	Chapter 9	Chapter 4	Chapter 6, Chapter 19	Chapter 6
Factors Influencing the Rate of Yeast Respiration	Chapter 8	Chapter 9	Chapter 5		Chapter 6
How can genetically engineered plants be multiplied?	Chapter 13	Chapter 13	Chapter 15	Chapter 28	Chapter 11
Making Test Crosses	Chapter 13	Chapter 13	Chapter 13	Chapter 26	Chapter 11
How is camouflage an adaptive advantage?	Chapter 15	Chapter 15		Chapter 29	Chapter 13
Biochemical Evidence for Evolution	Chapter 15	Chapter 15	Chapter 19	Chapter 29	Chapter 12
Transpiration in Plants	Chapter 22	Chapter 23	Chapter 3	Chapter 19	Chapter 21
The Human Heart	Chapter 34	Chapter 37	Chapter 7	Chapter 11	Chapter 21
Earthworm Behavior	Chapter 31	Chapter 33	Chapter 22	Chapter 17	
Field Studies of a Freshwater Ecosystem	Chapter 3	Chapter 3	Chapter 25	Chapter 31	
Testing Water Quality	Chapter 3, Chapter 5	Chapter 3, Chapter 5	Chapter 25	Chapter 32	Chapter 30

Safety and Disposal Guidelines

The activities in this manual are designed to minimize dangers in the laboratory. Even so, there are no guarantees against accidents. However, careful planning and preparation, as well as being aware of hazards, can help keep accidents to a minimum.

General Safety. Review general safety rules listed in the Student Edition of ***Biology Pre-AP Lab Manual.*** These general rules should be emphasized to students before any laboratory work is done and should be reviewed periodically.

Additional Safety Guidelines.

• At the beginning of the year, review the safety symbols used in all Glencoe Science Programs. Test students on their knowledge of these symbols.

• Review how to obtain all needed Material Safety Data Sheets. Print out all that will be needed for each lab.

In the Laboratory

1. Store chemicals properly.

  a. Separate chemicals by reaction type.

  b. Label all chemical containers: include purchase data, special precautions, and expiration date.

  c. Appropriately dispose of chemicals when outdated.

  d. Do not store chemicals above eye level.

  e. Wood shelving is preferable to metal. All shelving should be firmly attached to walls and have antiroll lips.

  f. Store only those chemicals that you plan to use.

  g. Hazardous substances require special storage containers.

2. Store equipment properly.

  a. Clean and dry all equipment before storing.

  b. Protect electronic equipment and microscopes from dust, humidity, and extremes in temperature.

  c. Label and organize all equipment.

3. Provide adequate work space for activities.

4. Provide adequate ventilation.

5. Post safety and evacuation guidelines and safety symbols.

6. Check to ensure that safety equipment is accessible and working properly.

7. Provide containers for disposing of chemicals, broken glass, other waste products, and biological specimens. Disposal methods must meet local guidelines.

8. Use hot plates for procedures requiring a heat source. If lab burners are used, a central shut-off valve for the gas supply should be accessible to you. Never use open flames when a flammable solvent is in the same room.

Before Each Activity

1. Perform activities yourself before assigning them to students to determine where students may have trouble. Previewing the activities in this manner also enables you to make note of symbols and safety cautions already incorporated into each activity.

2. Arrange the laboratory in such a way that equipment and supplies are easily accessible to students. Avoiding confusion where solutions and reagents are being dispensed.

3. Have available only equipment and supplies necessary to complete the assigned activity. This practice helps eliminate the problem of students doing unauthorized experiments.

4. Review with students the procedure to be followed for each activity. Emphasize cautions found in the activities. Make students aware of specific safety symbols that are listed in the materials section of each activity where potential safety problems may arise. Safety symbols that are used in all Glencoe science programs are shown on page vi of the Student Edition. Post the appropriate MSDS sheet for the lab.

5. Review what students should do if an accident occurs. If chemicals need to be disposed of in a special place, remind students of proper disposal methods. Be sure all students know proper procedures to follow if an accident should occur and the proper way to use fire extinguishers, fire blankets, showers, and eyewash fountains. This equipment should be well marked and easily accessible.

Safety and Disposal Guidelines, continued

During the Activity

1. Make sure that the laboratory is clean and free of clutter. Students' books, coats, and other personal items should be stored away from the laboratory tables.

2. Students should wear eye protection when heating substances or working with acids or bases that can cause burns. Many schools require that eye protection be worn at all times in the science laboratory. Know your school's policies and regulations and follow them.

3. Never allow students to work alone in the laboratory. If an accident should occur, there would be no one available to help the injured student.

4. Never allow students to use a scalpel or other cutting device with more than one sharp edge. When dissecting specimens, be sure students use dissecting pans to support their specimens. Hand-holding a specimen is "asking for" cuts.

5. If your microscopes require a separate light source, be sure students use proper lamps. Using reflected sunlight can damage the eye.

6. Use extreme caution if you use a pressure cooker for sterilization purposes. Turn off the heat source, remove the cooker, and allow the pressure to return to normal before opening the cover.

7. Students should never point the open end of a heated test tube toward anyone.

8. Remove broken or chipped glassware from use immediately. Use a whisk broom and dustpan to pick up broken glass. Large wads of wet cotton should be used to pick up small pieces of glass. Also immediately clean up any spills that may occur. Dilute concentrated solutions with water before removing.

9. Be sure all glassware that is to be heated is a heat-treated type that will not shatter. If a gas flame is to be used as a heat source, the glassware should be protected from direct contact with the flame through the use of a wire gauze.

10. Remind students that heated glassware looks cool several seconds after heating but can still cause burns for several minutes.

11. Prohibit eating and drinking in the laboratory.

After the Activity

1. Be sure that the laboratory is clean. All work surfaces and equipment should be cleaned thoroughly after use.

2. Be sure students dispose of chemicals and broken glassware properly. Provide a container marked "Broken Glass."

3. Be sure all hot plates and burners are turned off and disconnected before leaving the laboratory.

Disposal Guidelines

1. Bacterial and fungal cultures, used plastic petri dishes, cotton plugs, and contaminated growth medium should be autoclaved before disposal. Contaminated or used glassware should be autoclaved before being washed.

2. Obtain a current Material Safety Data Sheet (MSDS) for each chemical. Follow the chemical disposal recommendations. Be aware of local, state, and federal regulations for disposing of chemicals in municipal sewage systems or sanitary landfills.

3. Acids and bases may be neutralized by adding dilute sodium hydroxide to acids and dilute hydrochloric acid to bases until pH paper indicates that they are no longer strongly acidic or basic. Be aware that neutralization of strong acids and bases generates heat, so use caution by neutralizing slowly.

4. Follow MSDS recommendations for disposing of the organic chemicals used in this laboratory manual.

5. Solid wastes can be disposed of by placing them in a container suitable for disposal in a sanitary landfill. Be sure to follow applicable local regulations.

6. Broken glass should be placed in a separate, well-marked container.

Remember, a positive attitude toward safety on the part of students is imperative in operating a safe laboratory. Student attitude often reflects the teacher's attitude. Therefore, it is most important that you, as the teacher, always have a positive attitude toward safety and set good safety examples when conducting demonstrations and experiments.

Preparation of Solutions

Solutions are listed in the order in which they are used. Preparation procedures, cautions, and amounts to make also are included. You may want to plan several weeks ahead so you will have all of the solutions prepared.

Add solvents to the solutes. If a specific order of preparation is needed, it will be noted. Dissolve and mix thoroughly. **Never add water directly to concentrated acid.** Always add the acid to some water to be used and then continue diluting. Because the diluting process produces heat, it is advised that you add the acid slowly down a stirring rod as you gently stir.

Unless directed otherwise, use distilled water in preparation of solutions requiring water. Using tap water may give erroneous results.

Mix solutions in a beaker or a flask of greater capacity than the amount you are making. Usually 100- to 300-mL containers work well. It is better to make a little more than the exact amount needed because students may spill or waste some solution.

Many chemicals can be stored for several years. However, certain chemicals become extremely hazardous, even explosive, with age. Know the age limitations of stored chemicals and the safe means of disposal of all chemicals in the laboratory. Flammable, volatile, and explosive chemicals should be stored in special secure areas and cabinets.

Solutions, once prepared, can be stored in large screw-cap or stoppered bottles. Glass is better than plastic because glass reacts with fewer chemicals. Storage containers should be cleaned with a low-sudsing detergent and rinsed well in distilled water before use.

If possible, request your principal or department head to schedule some student laboratory assistants for your use. These students should be qualified to assist in lab preparations and instruction. They should be A/B students, mature, and responsible, and they should have taken a course in biology. The students should work directly under your supervision.

Lab	Solution	Preparation	Cautions
Lab 1	Potassium permanganate solutions	5% solution: Mix 25 g potassium permanganate in 475 mL water; dissolve. 1% solution: Mix 5 g potassium permanganate in 495 mL of water; dissolve. 0.1% solution: Mix 0.5 g potassium permanganate in 499.5 mL of water; dissolve.	Potassium permanganate is a strong skin irritant. Flush with water.
Lab 2	6% salt solution	6 g salt in 94 mL water; dissolve.	
Lab 3	5% skim milk agar	Add 2.0 g non-nutrient agar and 5.0 g skim milk powder to 100 mL of water.	
	0.2% starch agar	0.2% solution: Add 2 g agar and 0.2 g starch to 100 mL water. 0.4% solution: Add 2 g agar and 0.4 g starch to 100 mL water. 0.8% solution: Add 2 g agar and 0.8 g starch to 100 mL water.	

Preparation of Solutions, *continued*

Lab	Solution	Preparation	Cautions
Lab 3 *(cont.)*	Nutrient broth	Add 8 g nutrient broth to 1 L water, or add 5 g peptone and 3 g beef extract to 1 L distilled water. Add all contents to a large beaker. Heat to dissolve. Pour into test tubes and autoclave at 15 lb pressure for 15 minutes. Store in refrigerator.	
	Gram's iodine	Dissolve 1 g iodine crystals and 2 g potassium iodine in 300 mL distilled water.	Danger: Iodine vapor is toxic or extremely irritating. Dust is hazardous when inhaled or touched. Causes burns or skin irritations. Flush with water.
Lab 4	Fuelgen stain	Purchase from a biological supply house.	Do not inhale. Flush with water if body contact occurs.
	Methanol-acetic acid fixative	Add 1 part glacial acetic acid to 3 parts 100% methanol.	Prepare under fume hood, wearing goggles and rubber gloves. Poisonous and corrosive. Flush with water if body contact occurs.
	45% acetic acid	Add 45 mL acetic acid to 55 mL distilled water.	Poisonous, corrosive irritant. Vapor may be harmful. Avoid spilling. Flush with water if body contact occurs.
	3% hydrochloric acid	Carefully pour 3 mL concentrated hydrochloric acid into 97 mL distilled water.	Corrosive irritant. Flush with water if body contact occurs. Work under a fume hood, wearing gloves, goggles, and apron.
	Caffeine solutions	Stock caffeine solutions (6.6%): Add 238 mL distilled water to 2 g instant coffee. 0.1%: Mix 130 mL distilled water with 2 mL stock solution. 0.3%: Mix 126 mL distilled water with 6 mL stock solution. 0.5%: Mix 122 mL distilled water with 10 mL stock solution.	
Lab 7	Solvent	For 20 students: add 5 mL acetone to 45 mL petroleum ether.	Danger: Highly flammable, extremely explosive. Acetone is also an irritant to eyes, lungs, and skin. Buy and use only small quantities. Good ventilation is essential. Guard against fire and explosion. Material must be dated and disposed of promptly. Flush with water.
Lab 8	Solution A	20 g fructose in 80 mL water	
	Solution B	Distilled water (100 mL)	
	Solution C	20 g lactose in 80 mL water.	
	Solution D	20 g sucrose in 80 mL water.	
	Glucose solution	20 g glucose in 80 mL water.	

Preparation of Solutions, *continued*

Lab	Solution	Preparation	Cautions
Lab 9	0.1% detergent solution	Add 1 mL of liquid dishwashing detergent to 1 L of distilled water.	
	10% bleach solution	Add 100 mL of household bleach to 1 L of distilled water.	
	70% ethanol	Add 700 mL of ethanol to 300 mL of distilled water.	
	Sodium hydroxide (NaOH)	Add 1 ml of 1.0 molar solution to 9 mL of distilled water.	Sodium hydroxide is caustic. Avoid contact with eyes or skin. Flush with water if contact occurs.
	Hydrochloric acid (HCl)	Add 1 ml of 1.0 molar solution to 9 mL of distilled water.	Corrosive irritant. Flush with water if body contact occurs. Work under a hood, wearing gloves, goggles, and apron.
Lab 16	Phenolphthalein	Add 0.5 g phenolphthalein to 99.5 mL 95% ethyl alcohol.	Flammable. Eye irritant. Do not ingest. If body contact occurs, flush with water.
	0.4% sodium hydroxide	Add 0.4 g to 99.6 mL water	Sodium hydroxide is caustic. Avoid contact with eyes or skin. Flush with water if contact occurs.
	70% ethanol	Add 700 mL of ethanol to 300 mL of distilled water.	
Lab 17	2.9 M sodium sulfite solution	Add 25 g solid anhydrous sodium sulfite crystals (Na_2SO_3) to enough distilled water to make 100 mL of solution. Prepare the solution 24 h in advance of calibrating the dissolved oxygen probe to ensure all oxygen has been depleted.	Possible tissue irritant. Moderately toxic in solid form. Avoid contact with skin and eyes. Flush with water if body contact occurs.

Materials Supply List

Lab	Equipment	Expendables	Chemical Supplies	Biological Supplies

Lab 1	beaker (100-mL)
	forceps
	metric ruler
	razor blade (single-edge)
	clock or watch with second hand
	small beakers (4)
		wax pencil	solutions (500 mL each):
			  5% potassium permanganate
			  1% potassium permanganate
			  0.1% potassium
			    permanganate
			water
				potato

Lab 2	microscope microscope slides coverslips (2) dropper forceps		6% salt solution water	*Elodea* (water plant)

Lab 3	incubator
	sterile petri dishes (4)
		sterile cotton swabs (8)
		wax pencil
		autoclavable biohazard
		  bags
			disinfecting solution
			iodine solution (15 mL)
			agar (15 mL each):
			  5% skim milk
			  0.2% starch
			  0.4% starch
			  0.8% starch
			nutrient broth (40 mL)
			Gram's iodine (15 mL)
				broth cultures:
				  Bacillus cereus
				  Bacillus subtilis
				  Escherichia coli
				  yeast suspension

Lab 4	clock or watch
	mL glass jars (150-mL) (32)
	metric ruler (8)
	scalpels (8)
	microscope slides (32)
	coverslips (32)
	forceps
	compound light microscopes (8)
	graduated cylinders (25-mL) (2)
	test tubes (64)
	test-tube holders (8)
	test-tube racks (8)
	thermometers (8)
	hot plates (8)
	water bath
	clocks or watches (8)
	thermal mitts (8 pairs)
		toothpicks (2 boxes)
		paper towels (1 roll)
		wax pencils (8)
			caffeine solutions:
			  0.1%, 0.3%, 0.5%
			distilled water
			Feulgen stain
			methanol-acetic acid fixative
			3% hydrochloric acid
			45% acetic acid in a
			  dropper bottle (8)
				onion bulbs (32)

Lab 5	compound light microscopes (30)	drawing paper
		  (optional) (30 sheets)
		pencil (colored pencils
		  optional) (30)
				prepared slide of lily
				anther (30)

Lab 6	lamp (40-watt) razor blade (single edge) metric ruler metal stand glass rod test tube (large)	tape	sodium bicarbonate powder water, warm (room temperature)	*Elodea* (water plant)

Materials Supply List, *continued*

Lab	Equipment	Expendables	Chemical Supplies	Biological Supplies
Lab 7	cork thumbtack scissors small container test-tube holder glass rod metric ruler pipette forceps hot plate beaker (600-mL) beaker (400-mL) thermal mitts (2)	filter paper (5-cm-long strip)	water ethyl alcohol (80 mL) chromatography solvent (5 mL)	spinach (defrosted and well-drained)
Lab 8	droppers (4) test tubes (4) one-hole stoppers (4) graduated cylinder thermometer (Celsius scale) pins (4)	wax pencil clay (optional) tape cloth towel quart milk cartons with tops cut off (4) ice	20% glucose solution (24 mL) cold water warm water	yeast cake (small piece) yeast food A yeast food B yeast food C yeast food D
Lab 9	beaker (250-mL) stirring rod sterile razor scissors dropper bottle (250-mL) sterile petri dishes (5) glass jar with screw-cap lid (250-mL or larger) sterile forceps	marking pen pH meter or paper parafilm	prepackaged African violet medium table sugar 0.1% detergent solution 10% bleach solution 70% ethanol in spray bottle distilled water NaOH and HCl (as needed to adjust pH) agar powder sterile water (1L)	fresh African violet leaves (2)
Lab 10	anesthetic wands (8) stereomicroscope or hand lens (8) fine-tipped paintbrush (8) culture vials with foam plugs (16)	white index cards (8) wax pencils (8)	alcohol (8 vials) anesthetic (8 vials)	instant *Drosophila* medium (1 bag) culture of vestigial- winged fruit flies (8) culture of normal- winged fruit flies (8)
Lab 11	hole punches (8) plastic film canisters or petri dishes (30)	colored paper (8 sheets each of purple, brown, blue, green, tan, black, orange, red, yellow, and white) graph paper (60 sheets) piece of brightly colored, floral fabric (80 cm × 80 cm) (8)		
Lab 12	No materials needed			

Materials Supply List, *continued*

Lab	Equipment	Expendables	Chemical Supplies	Biological Supplies
Lab 13	burner iron stand test-tube clamp glass tubing (20 cm) rubber tubing (6-cm sections) (2) beaker (1 L) beaker to hold the "U" tube 5-mL pipettes (2) razor blade or scalpel electric fan spotlight	paper towels cord (10 cm)	petroleum jelly water	potted plant *Geranium* or *Coleus*
Lab 14	plastic bottle 2-hole stopper to fit bottle metric ruler glass tube (3 cm long) glass tube (18 cm long) plastic tube (15 cm long)			
Lab 15	scissors lamp metric ruler clock or watch with second hand	shoe box (or shoe box lid) paper towels black paper cardboard tape	water	live earthworms
Lab 16	hammer stakes or large nails (14) white lid from jar small jars (4) medium jars (4) large jars (4) sieve (large) net (1 × 2 meters) watch with second hand baby food jars (40) metersticks (3) Celsius thermometers (2) 100-mL sample bottles (1–2 dozen) pH kit hand lens (3) pipette (with 0.1-mL graduations) white enamel trays, large (2) forceps coverslips (3) glass slides (3) dropper (3) microscopes (3) stereomicroscopes (3) watch glass	graph paper (8 sheets) large plastic bags (1 dozen) wax pencil cord (100 m) capped plastic bottle	phenolphthalein (25 mL) 0.4% sodium hydroxide (50 mL) 70% ethyl alcohol (4–6 L)	

Materials Supply List, *continued*

Lab	Equipment	Expendables	Chemical Supplies	Biological Supplies

Lab 17	LabPro or CBL 2 unit
	AC adapter (optional)
	TI graphing calculator
	link cable
	Vernier dissolved oxygen probe
	Beral pipette
	dissolved oxygen
	  calibration bottle
	metric ruler
	classroom thermometer
	classroom barometer
	graduated cylinder (100-mL)
	graduated cylinder (10-mL)
	beakers (100-mL) (5)
	jars with lids (4 or more)
		wax pencil
		lab wipes
			sodium sulfite calibration
			  solution
			D.O. electrode filling
			  solution
			plastic or rubber gloves
			distilled water
				water samples from
				  different locations
				  (4 or more)

LAB MANUAL

Biology
Pre-AP

Glencoe Science
Pre-AP Series

Mc Graw Hill Glencoe

New York, New York   Columbus, Ohio   Chicago, Illinois   Peoria, Illinois   Woodland Hills, California

GLENCOE SCIENCE PRE-AP SERIES
Biology Pre-AP Lab Manual

Send all inquiries to:
Glencoe/McGraw-Hill
8787 Orion Place
Columbus, OH 43240-4027

ISBN 0-07-869730-1

Printed in the United States of America.

1 2 3 4 5 6 7 8 9 10   079   09 08 07 06 05 04

Contents

To the Student

How to Use This Laboratory Manual

Working in the laboratory throughout the course of the year can be an enjoyable part of your biology experience. *Biology Pre-AP Lab Manual* provides you with a variety of activities on a range of topics. The laboratory activities are designed to fulfill the following purposes:

- to stimulate your interest in science in general and especially in biology
- to reinforce important concepts studied in your textbook
- to allow you to verify some of the scientific information learned during your biology course
- to allow you to discover for yourself biological concepts and ideas not necessarily covered in class or in the textbook readings
- to acquaint you with a variety of modern tools and techniques used by today's biological scientists
- to develop the skills and concepts you need for AP courses

Most importantly, the laboratory activities will give you firsthand experience in how a scientist works.

In the activities in this manual, you will be presented with a problem. Then, through use of controlled scientific methods, you will seek answers. Your conclusions will be based on your experimental observations alone or on those made by the entire class, recorded data, and your interpretation of what the data and observations mean.

The general format of the activities in *Biology Pre-AP Lab Manual* is listed below. Understanding the purpose of each of these parts will help make your laboratory experiences easier.

1. **Introduction**—The introductory paragraphs give you background information needed to understand the activity.

2. **Objectives**—The list of objectives is a guide to what will be done in the activity and what will be expected of you.

3. **Materials**—The materials section lists the supplies you will need to complete the activity.

4. **Procedure**—The procedure gives you step-by-step instructions for carrying out the activity. Many steps have safety precautions. Be sure to read these statements and obey them for your own and your classmates' protection. Unless told to do otherwise, you are expected to complete all parts of each assigned activity. Important information needed for the procedure but that is not an actual procedural step also is found in this section.

5. **Data and Analysis**—This section includes tables and space to record data and observations. In this section, you also draw conclusions about the results of the activity just completed.

Pre-AP

The activities in this lab manual will help you prepare for an AP biology course by:

- teaching you to draw inferences
- teaching you the six levels of questioning: knowledge recall, comprehension, application, analysis, synthesis, and evaluation
- helping you to implement the yes–but strategy for analyzing an argument
- helping you to synthesize perspectives from different points of view

Safety

In addition to the activities, this laboratory manual has information on safety that includes first aid and a safety symbol chart. Read the section on safety now. Safety in the laboratory is your responsibility. Working in the laboratory can be a safe and fun learning experience. By using *Biology Pre-AP Lab Manual,* you will find biology both understandable and exciting. Have a good year!

Copyright © Glencoe/McGraw-Hill, a division of The McGraw-Hill Companies, Inc.

Laboratory and Safety Guidelines

Emergencies

- Inform the teacher immediately of *any* mishap—fire, injury, glassware breakage, chemical spills, and so forth.
- Know the location of the fire extinguisher, safety shower, eyewash, fire blanket, and first aid kit. Know how to use this equipment.
- If chemicals come into contact with your eyes or skin, flush with large quantities of water and notify your teacher immediately.

Preventing Accidents

- Do NOT wear clothing that is loose enough to catch on anything. Do NOT wear sandals or open-toed shoes. Remove loose jewelry—chains or bracelets—while doing lab work.
- Wear protective safety gloves, goggles, and aprons as instructed.
- Always wear safety goggles (not glasses) in the laboratory.
- Wear goggles throughout the entire activity, cleanup, and handwashing.
- Keep your hands away from your face while working in the laboratory.
- Remove synthetic fingernails before working in the lab (these are highly flammable).
- Do NOT use hair spray, mousse, or other flammable hair products just before or during laboratory work where an open flame is used (they can ignite easily).
- Tie back long hair and loose clothing to keep them away from flames and equipment.
- Eating, drinking, chewing gum, applying makeup, and smoking are prohibited in the laboratory.
- Do NOT inhale vapors or taste, touch, or smell any chemical or substance unless instructed to do so by your teacher.

Working in the Laboratory

- Study all instructions before you begin a laboratory or field activity. Ask questions if you do not understand any part of the activity.
- Work ONLY on activities assigned by your teacher. NEVER work alone in the laboratory.
- Do NOT substitute other chemicals or substances for those listed in your activity.
- Do NOT begin any activity until directed to do so by your teacher.
- Do NOT handle any equipment without specific permission.
- Remain in your own work area unless given permission by your teacher to leave it.
- Do NOT point heated containers—test tubes, flasks, and so forth—at yourself or anyone else.
- Do NOT take any materials or chemicals out of the classroom.
- Stay out of storage areas unless you are instructed to be there and are supervised by your teacher.

Laboratory Cleanup

- Keep work, lab, and balance areas clean, limiting the amount of easily ignitable materials.
- Turn off all burners, water faucets, probeware, and calculators before leaving the lab.
- Carefully dispose of waste materials as instructed by your teacher.
- With your goggles on, wash your hands thoroughly with soap and warm water after each activity.

Safety Symbols

The *Biology Pre-AP Lab Manual* program uses several safety symbols to alert you to possible laboratory dangers. These safety symbols are explained below. Be sure that you understand each symbol before you begin a lab activity.

SAFETY SYMBOLS	HAZARD	EXAMPLES	PRECAUTION	REMEDY
DISPOSAL	Special disposal procedures need to be followed.	certain chemicals, living organisms	Do not dispose of these materials in the sink or trash can.	Dispose of wastes as directed by your teacher.
BIOLOGICAL	Organisms or other biological materials that might be harmful to humans	bacteria, fungi, blood, unpreserved tissues, plant materials	Avoid skin contact with these materials. Wear mask or gloves.	Notify your teacher if you suspect contact with material. Wash hands thoroughly.
EXTREME TEMPERATURE	Objects that can burn skin by being too cold or too hot	boiling liquids, hot plates, dry ice, liquid nitrogen	Use proper protection when handling.	Go to your teacher for first aid.
SHARP OBJECT	Use of tools or glassware that can easily puncture or slice skin	razor blades, pins, scalpels, pointed tools, dissecting probes, broken glass	Practice common-sense behavior and follow guidelines for use of the tool.	Go to your teacher for first aid.
FUME	Possible danger to respiratory tract from fumes	ammonia, acetone, nail polish remover, heated sulfur, moth balls	Make sure there is good ventilation. Never smell fumes directly. Wear a mask.	Leave foul area and notify your teacher immediately.
ELECTRICAL	Possible danger from electrical shock or burn	improper grounding, liquid spills, short circuits, exposed wires	Double-check setup with teacher. Check condition of wires and apparatus.	Do not attempt to fix electrical problems. Notify your teacher immediately.
IRRITANT	Substances that can irritate the skin or mucous membranes of the respiratory tract	pollen, moth balls, steel wool, fiber glass, potassium permanganate	Wear dust mask and gloves. Practice extra care when handling these materials.	Go to your teacher for first aid.
CHEMICAL	Chemicals that can react with and destroy tissue and other materials	bleaches such as hydrogen peroxide; acids such as sulfuric acid, hydrochloric acid; bases such as ammonia, sodium hydroxide	Wear goggles, gloves, and an apron.	Immediately flush the affected area with water and notify your teacher.
TOXIC	Substance may be poisonous if touched, inhaled, or swallowed	mercury, many metal compounds, iodine, poinsettia plant parts	Follow your teacher's instructions.	Always wash hands thoroughly after use. Go to your teacher for first aid.
OPEN FLAME	Open flame may ignite flammable chemicals, loose clothing, or hair	alcohol, kerosene, potassium permanganate, hair, clothing	Tie back hair. Avoid wearing loose clothing. Avoid open flames when using flammable chemicals. Be aware of locations of fire safety equipment.	Notify your teacher immediately. Use fire safety equipment if applicable.

Eye Safety
Proper eye protection should be worn at all times by anyone performing or observing science activities.

Clothing Protection
This symbol appears when substances could stain or burn clothing.

Animal Safety
This symbol appears when safety of animals and students must be ensured.

Handwashing
After the lab, wash hands with soap and water before removing goggles.

Copyright © Glencoe/McGraw-Hill, a division of The McGraw-Hill Companies, Inc.

Pre-AP   Measuring Diffusion Rates

The cell membrane determines what substances can diffuse into a cell. This characteristic of a cell membrane is called permeability. Many cells are semipermeable. Some substances can pass through the cell membrane, but others cannot. A certain substance, potassium permanganate, can pass through a cell membrane. However, its diffusion into a cell is influenced by its concentration and the time allowed for diffusion.

OBJECTIVES

In this investigation, you will determine the effect of time and concentration on the diffusion of potassium permanganate into potato cubes.

MATERIALS

beaker (100-mL)

wax pencil

potato

razor blade (single-edge)

small beakers (4)

clock or watch with second hand

5% potassium permanganate solution

1% potassium permanganate solution

0.1% potassium permanganate solution

forceps

metric ruler

water

PROCEDURE

Part A: Influence of Time on Diffusion

1. With a razor blade, cut five cubes from a potato. Each cube should measure 1 cm on each side.

2. Place four of the five cubes into a small beaker half filled with 5% potassium permanganate solution (Figure 1). Note the exact time the cubes are added to the solution.

Figure 1

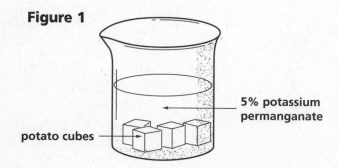

5% potassium permanganate

potato cubes

3. With forceps, remove one cube from the solution every ten minutes.

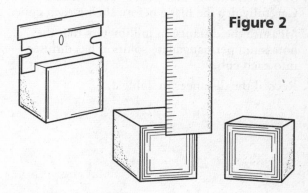

Figure 2

4. Slice each cube open with a razor blade (Figure 2). **CAUTION:** *Slice away from fingers to avoid cuts.* Carefully dry the razor blade before slicing each cube. Measure the distance in millimeters that the solution has diffused into each potato

Lab

1

Measuring Diffusion Rates

PROCEDURE continued

cube. Distances that you measure may not be very large.

5. Record the distance and total time in the solution for each cube in Table 1.

6. Slice open the cube that was not added to the solution. This cube will be your "control." Consider it as the zero minutes cube (Cube 1) in the table.

Part B: Influence of the Chemical Concentration on Diffusion

1. Pour equal amounts of the following liquids into separate beakers:

     5% potassium permanganate solution

     1% potassium permanganate solution

     0.1% potassium permanganate solution

Label each beaker as to the strength of liquid being used—5%, 1%, or 0.1%. Record the concentrations in Table 2.

2. Cut three potato cubes each measuring about 1 cm on a side.

3. Place one potato cube into each beaker (Figure 3). Note the exact time the cubes are added to the solutions.

4. After 40 minutes, use forceps to remove each potato cube from its solution.

5. Slice each cube in half with a razor blade. Carefully dry the blade before slicing each cube.

6. Measure the distance in millimeters that the potassium permanganate solution has diffused into each cube.

7. Record the distances in Table 2.

Figure 3

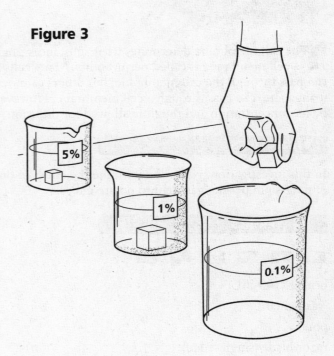

Measuring Diffusion Rates

DATA AND ANALYSIS

Table 1

	Potato Cubes in Solutions for Different Lengths of Time	
Cube	Time in Solution (min)	Distance of Diffusion (mm)
1	0	
2	10	
3	20	
4	30	
5	40	

Table 2

	Potato Cubes in Solutions of Different Concentrations	
Cube	Concentration of Chemical	Distance of Diffusion (mm)
1		
2		
3		

1. Diffusion results in the movement of chemicals through a permeable cell membrane from areas of high amount or concentration toward areas of low amount or concentration.

   (a) At the start, was iodine in high or low concentration outside of the bag?

   _____

   _____

   (b) At the start, was iodine in high or low concentration inside the bag?

   _____

   (c) Did iodine move by diffusion?

   _____

2. Some scientists believe that membranes contain very small pores. Pore size may determine why some chemicals can or cannot pass through a cell membrane. How might the size of the membrane pore compare to the size of.

   (a) the iodine molecules?

   _____

   (b) the starch molecules?

   _____

3. On a separate sheet of paper, write a paragraph which summarizes Part B of this investigation. Include (a) the purpose of Part B, (b) your investigation findings, and (c) how the length of time in the solution Q influences the amount of diffusion. Use specific values from Table 1 to support your statements.

4. On a separate sheet of paper, write a paragraph which summarizes Part C. Include (a) the purpose of Part C, (b) your investigation findings, and (c) how the concentration of a solution influences the amount of diffusion. Use specific values from Table 2 to support your statements.

Pre-AP Normal and Plasmolyzed Cells

Diffusion of water molecules across a cell's outer membrane from areas of high water concentration to areas of low water concentration is called osmosis. This movement of water may be harmful to cells. It can result in cell water loss (plasmolysis) when living cells are placed into an environment where the water concentration inside the cell is higher than outside the cell. However, most cells live in an environment where movement of water in and out of the cell is about equal. Therefore, there are no harmful effects to the cell.

OBJECTIVES

In this investigation you will

- prepare a wet mount of an *Elodea* leaf in tap water and a wet mount of an *Elodea* leaf in salt water for microscopic observation.

- observe and diagram cells of both wet mounts.

- observe the normal appearance of *Elodea* cells in tap water.

- compare normal cells in tap water to plasmolyzed cells in salt water.

MATERIALS

microscope   dropper
microscope slide   water
coverslips   6% salt solution
Elodea (water plant)   forceps

PROCEDURE

1. Prepare a wet mount of two *Elodea* leaves as follows. Use Figure 1 as a guide.

2. Put two or three drops of tap water on the left side of the slide.

3. Put two or three drops of 6% salt water on the right side of the slide.

4. Place one *Elodea* leaf in the water on each side of the slide.

5. Add coverslips to both leaves. NOTE: Make sure that the two liquids on the slide do not run together. If they do, discard leaves and start over using fewer drops of liquid.

6. Wait two or three minutes. Observe each leaf under both low and high powers. To observe both leaves, simply move the slide back and forth across the microscope stage.

7. Carefully observe the location of chloroplasts in relation to the cell wall of both leaves.

8. Diagram in the space provided under Data and Analysis a *single cell from each side*. Label the *cell wall*, *cell membrane*, and *chloroplasts* in both cells. (Be careful—can you see the cell membrane in both cells or only in one?)

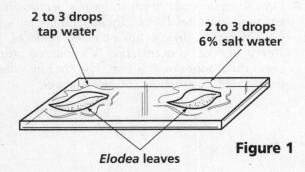

2 to 3 drops tap water

2 to 3 drops 6% salt water

Elodea **leaves**

Figure 1

Normal and Plasmolyzed Cells

DATA AND ANALYSIS

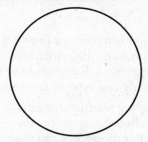

Normal plant cell

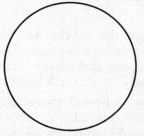

Plasmolyzed plant cell

Read the following four statements before answering the questions:

(a) *Elodea* cells normally contain 1% salt and 99% water on the inside.

(b) Tap water used in this investigation contains 1% salt and 99% water.

(c) Salt water used in this investigation contains 6% salt and 94% water.

(d) Salt water has a higher concentration of salt than fresh water or *Elodea* cells.

1. Describe the location of chloroplasts in a normal *Elodea* cell (in tap water).

_____

2. Describe the location of chloroplasts in a plasmolyzed cell (in salt water).

_____

3. Answer the following questions about the cell in tap water.

(a) What is the percentage of water outside the cell?

_____

(b) What is the percentage of water inside the cell?

_____

(c) How do the percentages compare?

_____

(d) Did the cell change shape? Explain.

_____

_____

4. Answer the following questions about the cell in salt water.

(a) What is the percentage of water outside the cell at the investigation's start?

_____

(b) What is the percentage of water inside the cell at the investigation's start?

_____

(c) Is the percentage of water (concentration) inside higher or lower than the percentage outside?

_____

(d) When will water move across the cell's membrane?

_____

(e) Should water move from high to low concentration or low to high concentration? Explain.

_____

_____

(f) Did the inside of the cell change shape due to water loss? Explain.

_____

_____

5. What is plasmolysis?

_____

_____

Lab 3

Pre-AP Extracellular Enzymes

Enzymes are catalysts that aid chemical reactions. A catalyst's function is to change the rate of reaction. Enzymes are composed of biological materials called proteins. Enzymes take part in necessary biochemical processes that occur in the cells of all organisms. Enzymes have a specific function to perform in a cell. In most cases, enzymes will aid only one type of reaction.

Some enzymes can move through the cell membrane into the surrounomg medium, or environment. Such an enzyme is called an extracellular enzyme. An extracellular enzyme breaks down (or digests) complex molecules into smaller molecules. The smaller molecules can then be absorbed through the cell membrane. These molecules can be metabolized within the cell for energy.

OBJECTIVES

In this investigation, you will distinguish the degree of extracellular digestion that occurs as a result of bacterial growth on agar plates containing starch or milk.

MATERIALS

broth cultures: wax pencil   0.4% starch agar (15 mL)
  Bacillus cereus   incubator   0.8% starch agar (15 mL)
  Bacillus subtilis   iodine solution (15 mL)   sterile cotton swabs (8)
  Escherichia coli   5% skim milk agar (15 mL)   sterile petri dishes (4)
  yeast suspension   0.2% starch agar (15 mL)

PROCEDURE

Part A: Hydrolysis (Digestion) of Starch

CAUTION: *Do not touch your eyes, mouth, or any other part of your face while doing this lab. Wear your laboratory apron and goggles. Wash your work surface with disinfectant solution, using a paper towel, both before and after doing the lab.*

1. Obtain a petri dish of each starch solution concentration. Divide each dish into four sectors by marking on the bottom of the dish with a wax pencil. Label each petri dish with your name and the starch concentration.

2. Inoculate each dish by dipping a sterile cotton swab into a broth culture, slightly opening the lid, and gently swabbing a sector of the starch agar in the dish (Figure 1). Using a new sterile swab for each culture, inoculate each sector of all four dishes. Place *B. subtilis* on sector 1, *E. coli* on sector 2, *B. cereus* on sector 3, and yeast on sector 4.

Figure 1

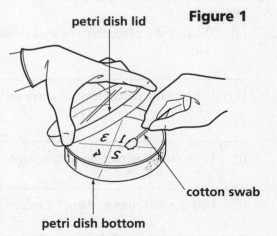

petri dish lid

cotton swab

petri dish bottom

Extracellular Enzymes

PROCEDURE continued

3. In your lab notebook, record the concentration of starch and the culture swabbed on each sector in a data table similar to Table 1.

4. Incubate the dishes inverted at 37°C for 48 hours.

5. Test each petri dish for starch hydrolysis by flooding the dish with iodine solution. **CAUTION:** *If iodine spillage occurs, rinse with water.* After one minute, drain off the iodine into a sink. An unstained area around a culture indicates digestion of starch by the organism.

6. Record which organisms did and did not digest starch. Record in your lab notebook whether starch digestion is affected by the concentration of starch in the plates. Record the degree of differences noted in each concentration in your data chart.

Part B: Hydrolysis (Digestion) of Milk Proteins

1. Obtain a skim milk agar dish. Divide the dish into four sectors by marking on the bottom of the dish with a glass marking pencil. Inoculate each sector with the different cultures as you did in Part A.

2. Label the petri dish with your name and "milk agar" to differentiate it from starch agar. In your lab notebook, record the culture swabbed on each sector in a data chart similar to Table 2.

3. Incubate the dish inverted for four days at 37°C to ensure maximum growth. A clear area immediately surrounding an area of growth is evidence of protein hydrolysis. Record which organisms did and did not digest protein in your data chart.

DATA AND ANALYSIS

Table 1

Hydrolysis of Starch		
% Starch	Culture Type	Observations

Table 2

Hydrolysis of Milk Proteins		
% Skim Milk	Culture Type	Observations

1. Why were the petri dishes inverted during incubation? (HINT: Consider the water droplets that condensed on the lids of the petri dishes.)

_____

2. Did any type of microorganism digest starch better than another? If so, which one?

_____

Extracellular Enzymes

> **PROCEDURE** continued

3. Is starch digestion gradual? Explain the evidence you have to support your answer.

_____

_____

4. Which microorganisms did not appear to digest starch at all?

_____

5. What does your answer to question 4 tell you about the enzyme used in starch digestion?

_____

_____

6. On which dish did starch digestion appear most complete? Explain your answer.

_____

_____

7. Which microorganisms appeared to digest milk proteins? Explain your answer.

_____

_____

8. Which microorganisms digested both starches and proteins? Why?

_____

_____

Pre-AP How does the environment affect mitosis?

Mitosis is the division of the nucleus of eukaryotic cells followed by the division of the cytoplasm (cytokinesis). If the division proceeds correctly, it produces two cells that are genetically identical to the original cell. Mitosis is responsible for the growth of an organism from a fertilized egg to its final size and is necessary for the repair and replacement of tissue. Anything that influences mitosis can impact the genetic continuity of cells and the health of organisms.

How do environmental factors affect the rate and quality of mitotic division? Scientists are perhaps most keenly interested in this question from the perspective of disease, specifically, the uncontrolled division of cells known as cancer. This investigation will allow you to make a simplified study of the relationship between the environment and mitosis.

OBJECTIVES

In this investigation, you will

- prepare squashes of onion root tips to observe mitosis.

- make a hypothesis to describe the effect of caffeine on mitosis.

- compare growth of onion roots in water and in caffeine.

MATERIALS

onion bulbs (4)
toothpicks (16)
150-mL glass jars (4)
concentrations of
    caffeine (coffee):
    0.1%, 0.3%, 0.5%
metric ruler
wax pencil

scalpel
paper towels
distilled water
microscope slides (4)
coverslips (4)
Feulgen stain
methanol-acetic
    acid fixative

3% hydrochloric acid
45% acetic acid in a
    dropper bottle
forceps
microscope
25-mL graduated
    cylinders (2)
test tubes (8)

test-tube holder
test-tube rack
thermometer
hot plate
water bath
clock or watch

PROCEDURE

Part A: Comparing Rates of Growth

1. Put on a laboratory apron and goggles. Label the small glass jars A, B, C, and D.

2. Insert a toothpick into opposite sides of each onion bulb so that each bulb can be balanced over the mouth of a jar, as shown in Figure 1. Then pour water into each jar until just the root area of the bulb is immersed. Wash your hands thoroughly.

3. Examine the bulbs each day. In Table 1, record the number of roots that emerge from each bulb and the average of their lengths.

Figure 1

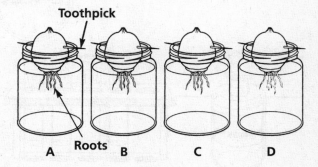

How does the environment affect mitosis?

How does the environment
affect mitosis?

PROCEDURE   continued

4. When the roots have grown to 1 cm in length, pour the water out of jars B, C, and D. Your teacher will provide you with caffeine solutions of three different concentrations. Fill jar B with the 0.1% solution, jar C with the 0.3% solution, and jar D with the 0.5% solution. Once again, balance the bulbs over the mouth of jars B, C, and D so that the roots are immersed.

5. Measure the roots for 3 more days, each time recording the average length of the roots for each of the treatments (that is, water and the three concentrations of caffeine) in Table 2.

Part B: Comparing Phases of Mitosis

Note: READ ALL STEPS BEFORE YOU START.

1. Label 4 test tubes A, B, C, and D to correspond to the treatments to which the onion bulbs are being subjected. Then pour 5 mL of methanol-acetic acid fixative into each of the tubes.

2. Set up and begin heating the water bath to 60°C.

3. Use the scalpel to remove all of the roots from each of the onion bulbs. **CAUTION:** *Use the scalpel with care. Cut away from your fingers.* Then use the scalpel to cut a 3 mm piece from the *tips* of each root. Immediately place these tips from onion bulbs treated in A, B, C, and D jars into the corresponding test tubes containing the methanol-acetic acid fixative.

4. Use the test-tube holder to place test tubes A–D into the water bath at 60°C for 15 minutes.

5. Carefully pour the fixative from each tube into a labeled container to be disposed of by the

teacher. Transfer the root tips from each tube to four new test tubes labeled A–D.

6. Pour 5 mL of 3% hydrochloric acid into each of the new test tubes in order to prepare the DNA for staining. **CAUTION:** *Hydrochloric acid is a strong acid and causes burns. Avoid contact with skin or eyes. Flush with water immediately if contact occurs and call the teacher.* Place the test tubes into the water bath at 60°C for 10 minutes.

7. Carefully pour the acid into a labeled empty beaker that the teacher has set aside for the acid. Add enough drops of Feulgen stain into each test tube to cover the roots. **CAUTION:** *The stain can discolor your clothes and skin. Use it with care.* Let the tissues sit in the stain for 15 minutes.

8. From tube A, remove one root tip with a pair of forceps. Place the root tip in the center of a labeled slide. Add one or two drops of acetic acid. **CAUTION:** *If acetic acid is spilled, flush with water immediately and call the teacher.* Then place a coverslip over the specimen.

9. Place the slide on a paper towel cushion and cover the slide and coverslip with a piece of paper towel. Push down onto the coverslip with the eraser of a pencil. This is called a squash. *Do not press too hard or you will break the coverslip.*

10. Repeat steps 8 and 9 for treatments B, C, and D.

11. Make a hypothesis to describe the effect of caffeine on the stages of mitotic division. Write your hypothesis in the space provided under Data and Analysis.

Figure 2

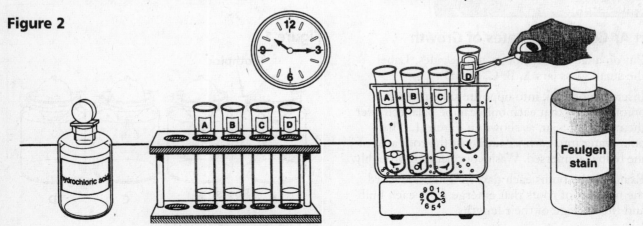

How does the environment affect mitosis?

PROCEDURE continued

12. Look at your slides under the microscope at low and high powers for cells undergoing mitosis. The cells will not be as neatly arranged as they would be on prepared slides. Examine the size, shape, and position of chromosomes in each treatment in order to help you identify phases of mitosis. In comparing treatments, do you notice differences in the number of cells in each phase? In the stronger caffeine solutions, do the chromosomes in any particular phase seem especially distinct? Count and record in Table 3 the number of cells in each phase of mitosis.

13. On a sheet of paper, sketch the stages of mitosis observed from roots in each treatment.

DATA AND ANALYSIS

Table 1

	Number of Roots and Average Length in Water							
	Bulb A		Bulb B		Bulb C		Bulb D	
Day	Number	Avg. Length	Number	Avg. Length	Number	Avg. Length	Number	Avg. Length
1								
2								
3								

Table 2

	Number of Roots and Average Length							
	Bulb A (water)		Bulb B (0.1%)		Bulb C (0.3%)		Bulb D (0.5%)	
Day	Number	Avg. Length	Number	Avg. Length	Number	Avg. Length	Number	Avg. Length
1								
2								
3								

Table 3

	Number of Mitotic Phases in Each Treatment					
Treatment	Interphase	Prophase	Metaphase	Anaphase	Telophase	Cytokinesis
Bulb A						
Bulb B						
Bulb C						
Bulb D						

Lab 4

How does the environment affect mitosis?

DATA AND ANALYSIS continued

1. Write your hypothesis.

_____

_____

2. Identify the control and variable for the experiment.

_____

_____

3. Study Tables 1 and 2. Compare the rate of growth of the roots immersed in water with the rate of root growth in the various concentrations of caffeine.

_____

_____

4. Describe any differences in the number of cells in each mitotic phase among the four squashes.

_____

_____

_____

5. How do your observations about mitotic phases in Part B relate to your observations about rate of root growth in Part A?

_____

_____

6. What are some conditions or factors in the environment that might have an effect upon the rate or quality of mitotic division?

_____

_____

7. Was your hypothesis supported by your data? Why or why not?

_____

_____

Pre-AP   **Lab 5**

Observation of Meiosis

Meiosis is a type of cell division that reduces the number of chromosomes to half the number found in body cells. This reduction in chromosome number occurs during gamete production and is necessary in order to maintain a stable number of chromosomes in cells from generation to generation. In flowering plants, meiosis results in the formation of male and female gametes. The male gametes are produced in the anthers of a flower.

OBJECTIVES

In this investigation, you will

- observe the stages of meiosis in lily anthers.
- draw and label the stages of meiosis in lily anthers.

MATERIALS

compound light microscope
prepared slide of a lily anther
drawing paper (optional)

pencil (colored pencils if desired)

PROCEDURE

1. Place a prepared slide of a lily anther on the microscope under low power.

2. Locate cells in the anther that are undergoing meiosis.

3. Choose a cell in meiosis and identify the stage of meiosis the cell is in by comparing it with the stages in Figure 1.

4. In the space provided in Data and Analysis, draw the cell and label it with the name of the appropriate stage of meiosis.

5. Continue to observe, identify, and draw cells for as many different stages of meiosis as you can find.

Figure 1

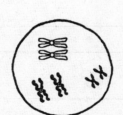
Prophase I

Late Prophase I

Metaphase I

Anaphase I

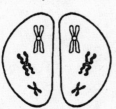
Telophase I

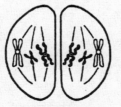
Metaphase II

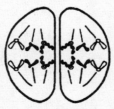
Anaphase II

Telophase II

Observation of Meiosis

DATA AND ANALYSIS

Student Cell Drawing

1. Why do you think lily anthers were chosen for this observation?

_____

_____

2. Which stages of meiosis did you observe most frequently?

_____

_____

3. Describe the chromosomes as they appear in the anther cells.

_____

_____

4. What is the overall function of meiosis in lily anthers?

_____

_____

Pre-AP Influencing the Rate of Photosynthesis

The overall equation for photosynthesis is written as

$$6CO_2 + 6H_2O \xrightarrow[\text{light}]{\text{enzymes, chlorophyll}} C_6H_{12}O_6 + 6O_2$$

In words, this says that carbon dioxide combines with water to form glucose and oxygen. This chemical change will take place if chlorophyll, certain enzymes, and light energy are present. Oxygen that is produced in photosynthesis is given off as a gas. If a lot of oxygen is being given off, photosynthesis is occurring rapidly. If little oxygen is being given off, photosynthesis is occurring slowly.

OBJECTIVES

In this investigation you will

- assemble the equipment needed to measure the rate of photosynthesis in *Elodea*.

- count bubbles of oxygen gas given off by *Elodea* to determine the rate of photosynthesis.

- change the conditions of photosynthesis by altering light intensity and carbon dioxide amount, and determine the effects on photosynthesis rate.

- prepare a bar graph of your collected data, and analyze it.

MATERIALS

Elodea (water plant)
test tube (large size)
water, warm (room temperature)
sodium bicarbonate powder
lamp (40 watt)

tape
razor blade (single-edge)
metric ruler
metal stand
glass rod—17 cm long

PROCEDURE

Part A: Setting Up the Experiment

1. Obtain a sprig of *Elodea*. Remove several leaves from around the cut end of the stem. Slice off a small portion of the stem at an angle and lightly crush the cut end of the stem as shown in Figure 1-A and 1-B. **CAUTION:** *Blade is sharp. Cut away from your fingers.*

2. Loosely wrap the *Elodea* around a glass rod. Slide the plant and tube into a test tube filled with *warm* water. Make sure that the cut and crushed end is toward the top of the test tube and below the water's surface.

Figure 1

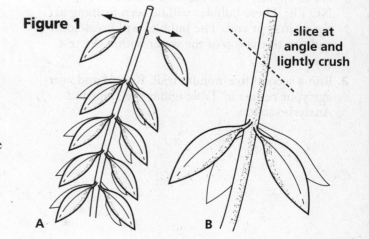

slice at angle and lightly crush

A   B

Influencing the Rate of Photosynthesis

PROCEDURE continued

Figure 2

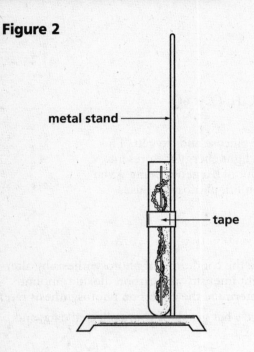

metal stand

tape

Figure 3

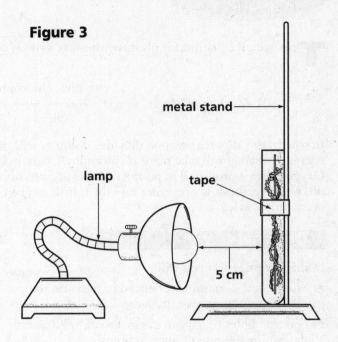

metal stand

lamp

tape

5 cm

3. Secure the test tube to a metal stand with tape as shown in Figure 2.

Part B: Running the Experiment

1. Place a 40-watt lamp 5 cm from the plant. Note the lamp's position in Figure 3. After several minutes count and record in Table 1 the number of oxygen bubbles rising from the cut end of the stem. Count bubbles for five minutes. If bubbles fail to appear, cut off more of the stem recrush. NOTE: These bubbles will be seen forming at the stem's cut end. The bubbles will break loose and rise to the top of the water within the test tube.

2. Run a second five-minute trial. Record and average your results in Table under the Data and Analysis section.

3. Move the lamp so it is 20 cm from the plant. After several minutes, count and record bubbles for two five-minute trials. Again, average and record your results in Table 1.

4. Add a pinch of sodium bicarbonate powder to the test tube. Place the lamp 5 cm from the test tube. After several minutes, record bubbles for two five-minute trials. Average and record your results in Table 1.

5. Prepare a bar graph of your results (use the space provided under Data and Analysis). Use the average number of bubbles for the vertical axis. Use the type of environmental condition for the horizontal axis. NOTE: You will have to figure out a proper scale to use along the vertical axis.

Influencing the Rate of Photosynthesis

DATA AND ANALYSIS

Environmental Condition	Number of Oxygen Bubbles		
	Trial 1	Trial 2	Trial 3
Lamp 5 cm from plant			
Lamp 20 cm from plant			
Plant in sodium bicarbonate; Lamp 5 cm away			

Student Bar Graph

1. What is being used in this investigation to determine the rate at which photosynthesis is occurring?
_____

2. (a) How did the number of oxygen bubbles (rate of photosynthesis) change as the light source was moved from a distance of 5 cm to 20 cm? _____

(b) What does this change tell you about the amount of light being received by the *Elodea* plant?
_____
_____

(c) How does the amount of light received by *Elodea* change the rate at which photosynthesis occurs?
_____
_____

3. (a) How did the rate of photosynthesis change when sodium bicarbonate was added to the *Elodea* plant 5 cm from the light? _____
_____

(b) Sodium bicarbonate adds carbon dioxide gas to the water. Why would the addition of sodium bicarbonate increase the rate of photosynthesis? _____

Lab 6

Influencing the Rate of Photosynthesis

DATA AND ANALYSIS continued

A series of line graphs was prepared by a student to help explain experimental results. Figure 5 shows the results after the student placed a 40-watt bulb 5 cm away from the plant. On each of the following graphs draw a line showing that which is indicated above the graph. In the space beside each graph, explain your reasons for drawing the graph line as you did.

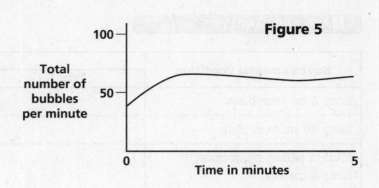

Figure 5

(a)   Show results if an 80-watt bulb were placed 5 cm away from the plant.

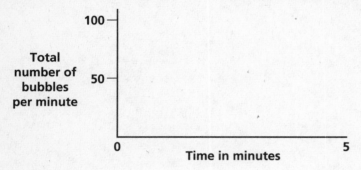

_____

_____

_____

(b)   Show results if no light at all had been used.

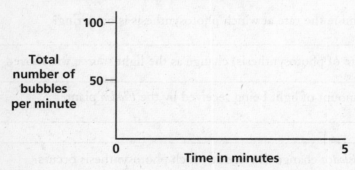

_____

_____

_____

(c)   Show results if a 40-watt bulb were placed 20 cm away from the plant.

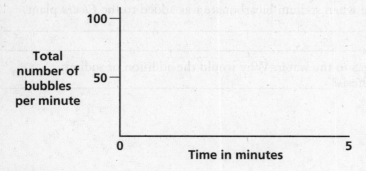

_____

_____

_____

Pre-AP Chloroplast Pigment Analysis

When you look at chloroplasts under a microscope or examine a plant leaf, the only color which appears to be present is a green pigment called chlorophyll. However, there are other pigments in a leaf. Yellow and orange pigments, not normally seen, are usually present within chloroplasts.

OBJECTIVES

In this investigation, you will

- remove pigments from spinach by boiling it in water and then heating it in ethyl alcohol.

- separate the pigments from one another by using a technique called chromatography.

- identify the pigments by their colors and positions on the chromatogram.

- determine relative amounts of each pigment.

MATERIALS

test tube holder	glass rod	beaker (600 mL)
filter paper (strip type)	water	ethyl alcohol
cork	metric ruler	beaker (400 mL)
thumbtack	glass pipette	small container
spinach (frozen package that has been defrosted)	forceps	
solvent	scissors	
	hot plate	

PROCEDURE

NOTE: One member of your class or your teacher may wish to prepare the pigment solution (Part A). From this preparation, enough pigment will be made available for the entire class. Each class member will then prepare his/her own chromatogram in Parts B and C

Part A: Preparing Leaf Pigments

1. Fill a 600 mL beaker 1/4 full of water. Set this beaker on a hot plate. **CAUTION:** *Always be careful when using a hot plate.*

2. Bring the water to a boil.

3. Place entire package of spinach into the boiling water. Bring to a boil again.

4. After several minutes, remove the beaker from the hot plate using the mitts to protect your hands. Remove the spinach from the water with

forceps and <u>squeeze out all excess water</u>. This step is very important. Then transfer the boiled spinach to a 400 mL beaker containing 80 mL of ethyl alcohol.

5. Heat the beaker by placing it onto the hot plate. Leave it on the hot plate for only about 30 seconds or until the alcohol begins to bubble. Remove the beaker using the mitts to protect your hands. Allow the alcohol to cool. Then reheat it several more times. **CAUTION:** *Alcohol is flammable. Do not spill it. If spillage occurs, turn off the hot plate and call your teacher immediately.*

6. Remove the beaker from the hot plate. **CAUTION:** *Beaker is hot. Do not touch the beaker with unprotected bands.* Squash the spinach with a glass rod. Reheat and squash until the alcohol solution becomes a dark green color. Enough pigment is now available for the entire class.

Chloroplast Pigment Analysis

PROCEDURE continued

Part B: Preparing the Chromatogram Chamber

Prepare your chromatogram chamber by following these steps.

1. Obtain a strip of filter paper at least 5 cm long.

2. Use scissors to taper the bottom of one end of the paper to a point. **CAUTION:** Always be careful when using scissors.

3. Cut two small notches about 2 cm from the bottom as shown in Figure 1.

4. Attach the filter paper strip to a cork using a

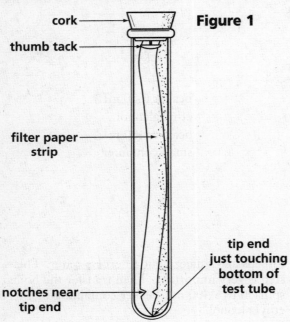

Figure 1

cork
thumb tack
filter paper strip
notches near tip end
tip end just touching bottom of test tube

thumbtack and position the strip so that when inserted into a test tube, the filter paper tip just touches the bottom. Adjust the height by moving the strip either up or down on the cork.

5. Your completed chamber should look like Figure 1.

Part C: Preparing the Chromatogram

Prepare your filter paper strip by following these steps.

1. Remove the filter paper strip from the tube and place it on your desk.

2. Add chlorophyll pigment to the paper strip

between the two notches as shown in Figure 2. Follow the procedure in Step 3.

3. To add chlorophyll to the paper, dip the fine end

Figure 2

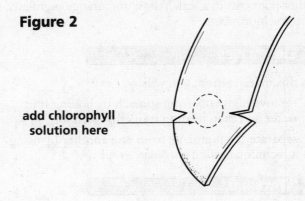

add chlorophyll solution here

of a tiny glass pipette into the chlorophyll solution provided. The pipette will fill by itself. Hold it in the chlorophyll solution only for an instant.

4. Touch the pipette to the correct location on the filter paper and quickly remove it. The chlorophyll solution should flow onto the paper. A small circle of solution the size of a pencil is ideal. Use Figure 3 as a guide.

5. Allow the spot to dry (about 30 seconds). Then add more pigment solution to the same spot. Make 20 applications of the solution. Allow time for drying between applications.

Figure 3

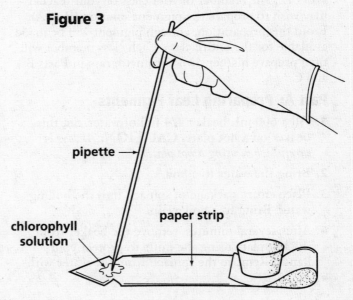

pipette
chlorophyll solution
paper strip

Chloroplast Pigment Analysis

PROCEDURE continued

Part D: Separating the Pigments

**CAUTION: SOLVENT IS HIGHLY FLAMMA-
BLE.** *Before proceeding, all flames in the laboratory
must be extinguished. Make sure the room is well-venti-
lated. Do not inhale fumes.*

1. Add solvent to a height of 0.5 cm in the test tube.

2. Carefully place the test tube into the test tube rack.

3. Place the filter paper strip into the tube. It is
important that the pointed tip dip into the solvent. Do not let the circle of chlorophyll touch
the solvent. Use Figure 4 as a guide.

4. DO NOT move or shake the tube for at least 15
minutes. Remove the paper chromatogram from
the test tube when the level of solvent almost
reaches the top of the paper strip.

5. Examine the chromatogram for the presence of
different bands of color. Each color band is a
different pigment.

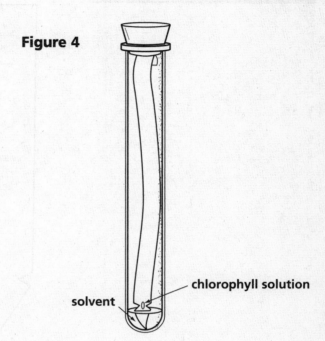

Figure 4

chlorophyll solution

solvent

DATA AND ANALYSIS

1. Describe the appearance of the filter paper strip at the conclusion of the experiment.

_____

_____

2. (a)   Is chlorophyll composed of one or several pigments? _____

   (b)   What proof do you have? _____

3. What is the value of chromatography?

_____

_____

_____

4. Examine your chromatogram strip. Each color band is a different pigment. Listed in order from top to
bottom on an ideal chromatogram are

Carotene—orange in color

Xanthophyll—yellow in color

Chlorophyll *a*—bright green in color

Chlorophyll *b*—a dull or khaki green in color

NOTE: Usually the two chlorophylls are very close to one another.

   (a)   How many different pigments can be seen on your chromatogram? _____

   (b)   Name the pigments which are present. _____

_____

Lab 7

Chloroplast Pigment Analysis

DATA AND ANALYSIS continued

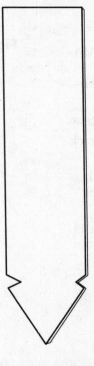

(c)   Use this outline diagram to draw and label the pigments on your chromatogram.

5. Using the amount of pigments present on your chromatogram,

(a)   which pigments are present in the smallest amounts in the leaf? _____

_____

(b)   which pigments are present in the greatest amounts in the leaf? _____

_____

6. Use your text (if necessary) to answer the following questions.

(a)   In what organelle (cell part) does one find leaf pigments? _____

(b)   What is the role of chlorophyll *a*? _____

_____

(c)   What is the role of carotene and xanthophyll?. _____

_____

7. How might the distribution of leaf pigments differ in a leaf that is dark green in color versus one which is light green in color?

_____

8. Many leaves change color in the autumn. How is it possible for this color change to happen? Base your answer on your new knowledge of pigments present in chloroplasts. (HINT: Chlorophyll *a* and chlorophyll *b* are easily broken down by the cooler autumn temperatures.)

_____

_____

Lab 8

Pre-AP   Factors Influencing the Rate of Yeast Respiration

All living systems respire. During respiration, food, usually in the form of glucose, is "burned." One of the products of respiration is carbon dioxide. The amount of carbon dioxide released during respiration indicates the respiration rate.

OBJECTIVES

In this investigation, you will
- count and record bubbles of carbon dioxide gas given off by respiring yeast cells.
- compare respiration rates at two different temperatures.
- compare respiration rates when using different foods for the yeast cells.

MATERIALS

yeast cake
droppers (4)
test tubes (4)
one-hole stoppers to fit test tubes (4)
20% glucose solution
cold water
clay (optional)

ice
straight pins (4)
tape
warm water
thermometer (Celsius scale)
wax pencil
quart milk cartons with tops cut off (2)

yeast food A
yeast food B
yeast food C
yeast food D
cloth towel
graduated cylinder

PROCEDURE

Part A: Influence of Temperature on Yeast Respiration Rate

NOTE: Work in pairs.

1. Remove the rubber bulbs from two droppers.

2. Wet the glass portion of each dropper. Push the small ends of the droppers into the small ends of two one-hole stoppers (Figure 1).
CAUTION: *Be careful not to break the glass. A gentle twisting motion works best. Wrap your hands in a cloth towel while inserting the droppers into the stoppers.*

3. To each of two test tubes, add a 1-cm cube of yeast and 12 mL of 20% glucose solution.

4. Mix the contents of each test tube making sure that the yeast cube has dissolved.

Figure 1

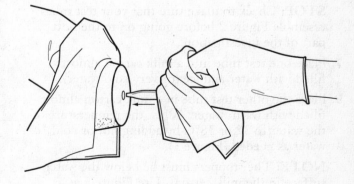

Lab
8

Factors Influencing the Rate of Yeast Respiration

5. Add a stopper with a dropper to each of the test tubes (Figure 2). Make sure all seals are tight.

Figure 2

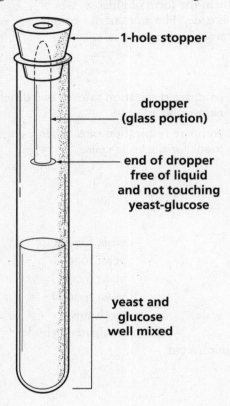

1-hole stopper

dropper (glass portion)

end of dropper free of liquid and not touching yeast-glucose

yeast and glucose well mixed

Figure 3

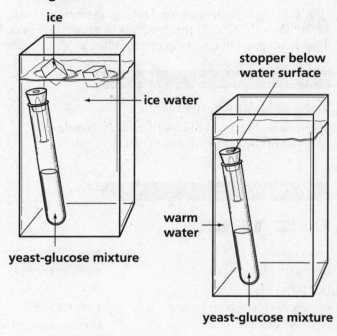

ice

ice water

stopper below water surface

warm water

yeast-glucose mixture

yeast-glucose mixture

6. Be sure that the ends of the droppers are not in the liquids. If necessary, pour enough liquid from the test tubes to keep the dropper above the liquid (see Figure 2).

STOP: Check to make sure that your test tubes resemble Figure 2 before going on to the next part of the investigation.

7. Place one test tube into a milk carton almost filled with water and ice (or very cold water).

8. Place the other test tube in a milk carton almost filled with warm water. Adjust the temperature of the water to 37 or 38°C by adding hot or cold water as needed (Figure 3).

NOTE: The stoppers must be below the water surface in the milk cartons. Use Figure 3 as a guide. If test tubes float or tip over, add a small plug of clay to the outside bottom of each test tube.

9. Measure the temperature of the water in each carton and record it in Table 1 under the Data and Analysis section.

10. Allow the tubes to sit undisturbed for two minutes. Then count the number of bubbles that rise from the opening of each stopper per minute for 10 minutes. Each team member should be responsible for counting the bubbles that rise from one test tube.

11. Record the number of bubbles in the first two columns of Table 1.

Part B: Influence of Different Foods on Yeast Respiration Rates

1. Prepare four stoppers and four test tubes as in Part A. Place a yeast cube into each tube. Add 12 mL of "Food A" into one tube. Label this tube "A." Mix the yeast and food.

2. Place 12 mL of "Food B" into the second tube, 12 mL of "Food C" into the third tube, and 12 mL of "Food D" into the fourth tube. Label the tubes. Mix all tubes so that the yeast dissolves.

Factors Influencing the Rate of Yeast Respiration

Figure 5

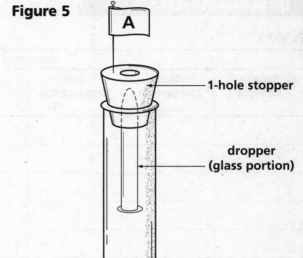

PROCEDURE continued

3. Prepare four pin markers as follows. Wrap a piece of tape around a pin (Figure 4). Label this marker "A." Prepare three more markers, labeling them "B," "C," and "D." These markers will help you identify which tube (or tubes) are giving off carbon dioxide bubbles.

Figure 4

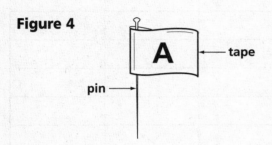

4. Add a stopper with a dropper to each of the four tubes. Insert the pin markers into the stoppers of the proper tubes (Figure 5).

   STOP: Check to make sure that

   (a) yeast and food are well mixed.

   (b) the end of the dropper closest to yeast-food mixture is free of liquid.

5. Place all four tubes into a milk carton filled almost to the top with water adjusted to between 38 and 40°C (Figure 6).

6. Again make sure that the stoppers are below the water surface. Use Figure 6 as a guide.

7. Allow the test tubes to sit undisturbed for two minutes. Then count the number of bubbles per minute that rise from each test tube for 10 minutes. Each team member should be responsible for counting the bubbles from two test tubes.

8. Record the number of bubbles in Table 1.

Part C: Comparing Class and Individual Data

9. Complete Table 2 by recording the total number of bubbles recorded by your team for Parts A and B.

10. Totals for each team should then be posted on the chalkboard and class averages determined. Record class averages for Parts A and B in Table 2.

Figure 6

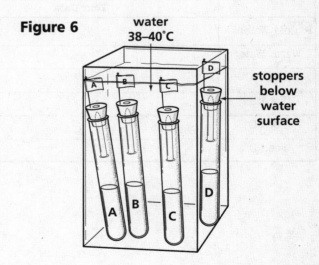

Factors Influencing the Rate of Yeast Respiration

DATA AND ANALYSIS

Table 1

	Number of Bubbles Per Minute					
Time in Minutes	Warm Temperature ___°C	Cold Temperature ___°C	Food A	Food B	Food C	Food D
1						
2						
3						
4						
5						
6						
7						
8						
9						
10						

Table 2

	Total Bubbles in 10 Minutes	
	Your Data	Class Average
Cold Water		
Warm Water		
Food A		
Food B		
Food C		
Food D		

Factors Influencing the Rate of Yeast Respiration

DATA AND ANALYSIS continued

1. Write a paragraph to summarize Part A of this investigation. Include (a) the purpose of Part A, (b) how respiration rate was measured, (c) the type of living organism used in this investigation, (d) how different temperatures of water influenced the respiration rate, of your yeast (use specific data from your results to help support your statements), (e) an explanation for why respiration rates may differ with different temperatures, (f) an explanation of how class averages compare in general to your individual team's data, and (g) several reasons your data and class averages may not agree exactly.

_____

_____

_____

_____

_____

2. Write a paragraph to summarize Part B of this investigation. Include all of the points listed above. However, remember that you are comparing the influence of different foods supplied to your yeasts on respiration rate.

_____

_____

_____

_____

_____

3. A student wishes to estimate the amount of ATP formed during Parts A and B of this experiment. However, they do not have any means for measuring ATP directly. Advise them on how they might judge ATP amounts produced,

_____

_____

_____

_____

4. It appears in Part B that the type of sugar used as food during yeast respiration does make a difference. Suggest a change in the experimental procedure that would allow you to determine which sugar types (monosaccharide, disaccharide, or polysaccharide) are the best food source.

_____

_____

_____

_____

Pre-AP   How can genetically engineered plants be multiplied?

DNA Transfer New genetic traits can be incorporated into an organism by directly transferring DNA from another organism. DNA can be transferred to plants by "shooting" them with a particle gun or by infecting plant tissues with a bacterium that then incorporates part of its DNA into the DNA of the host plant. In both methods, the DNA is transferred to a tiny fragment of plant tissue or a small mass of plant cells. Once the DNA has been transferred, the only way to regenerate new plants from such small pieces of tissue or clumps of cells is with tissue culture using micropropagation methods.

Micropropagation Micropropagation differs from all other plant propagation techniques in requiring aseptic conditions, conditions that are sterile or free of contamination by microorganisms, in order to be successful. The growing medium promotes the growth of bacteria and fungi spores, which are commonly found on surfaces and in the air. If the plant tissue cultures are contaminated by these organisms, they will grow rampantly and destroy or infect the plant tissues in the same culture.

OBJECTIVES

In this investigation, you will use micropropagation to produce new shoots from tiny pieces of African violet leaves.

MATERIALS

Everyday Materials
prepackaged medium-
    sized African violet
table sugar
fresh African violet
    leaves (2)
0.1% detergent
    solution

10% bleach solution
sterile razor blade
scissors
marking pen

Lab Materials
protective gloves
70% ethanol in spray
    bottle

distilled water
beaker (250 mL)
stirring rod
pH meter or paper
dropper
NaOH and HCl (as
    needed to adjust pH)
bottle (250 mL)

agar powder
sterile petri dishes (5)
250-mL or larger
    glass jar with
    screw-cap lid
1 L sterile water
sterile forceps
parafilm

PROCEDURE

Part A: Creating an Aseptic Environment

1. Put on a pair of protective gloves. Spray them with 70% ethanol before starting the procedure, and then respray them whenever you touch any nonsterile surface or material throughout the remainder of the procedure.

2. Spray your work surface with 70% ethanol. Also, spray all containers before placing them on the work surface as you carry out the procedure.

Part B: Preparing the Culture Medium

3. Place about 50 mL of distilled water, 0.58 g of prepackaged African violet medium, and 3.75 g of table sugar into a 250-mL beaker.

4. Add distilled water to bring the solution up to 100 mL. Stir until the sugar and African violet medium are dissolved.

5. Check the pH using a pH meter or paper. Add a few drops of NaOH or HCl as supplied by your teacher as needed to bring the pH between 5.6 and 5.8.

6. Add more distilled water to bring the solution up to 125 mL.

7. Pour the solution into a 250-mL bottle and add 1.0 g of agar powder.

8. Keeping the cap loose on the bottle, sterilize it by placing it in boiling water for 30 minutes.

Lab 9

How can genetically engineered plants be multiplied?

PROCEDURE continued

9. Remove the bottle from the hot water bath and gently swirl the medium to mix the agar until it is completely dissolved.

10. After the medium cools to about 50°C, pour about 25 mL into each of four sterile petri dishes. Store the dishes in their sleeves in the refrigerator until you need them in Part D of the *Procedure*.

Part C: Disinfecting the Leaves

11. Put the African violet leaves in the screw-cap jar and half-fill the jar with 0.1% detergent solution. Cap the jar tightly and gently agitate it for 3 minutes.

12. Pour off the detergent solution and rinse the leaves and jar with cool tap water.

13. Repeat step 11, substituting 10% bleach solution for detergent solution and gently agitate it for 10 minutes.

14. Pour off the bleach solution into the sink while keeping the lid loosely in place over the jar. Be careful not to pour out the leaves along with the bleach solution. The leaves should now be sterile. From this point on, prevent them from becoming contaminated by using only sterile water and sterile tools on them.

15. Spray the outside of the jar with 70% ethanol and place it on your sterile work surface.

16. Remove the lid from the jar and pour sterile water over the leaves until the jar is about half-full. Replace the lid and gently shake the jar for 2 minutes. Carefully pour off the rinse water into the sink without touching the leaves or removing them from the jar.

17. Repeat step 16 three times for a total of four sterile water rinses.

Part D: Preparing Leaf Tissue Cultures

18. Using the forceps, place the leaves on the remaining empty sterile petri dish. Hold the leaves with the forceps while you use the razor blade to cut them into squares about 1.5 cm on a side.

19. Place two or three strips of leaf into a dish of medium. Gently press the pieces against the medium with the forceps. Replace the cover on the dish and wrap it with a piece of parafilm, stretching the film to seal it. You and your partner should each prepare two dishes in this way. Label your two dishes with your initials and number them *one* and *two*.

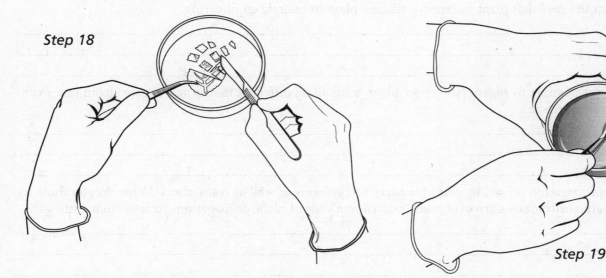

Step 18

Step 19

Lab 9

How can genetically engineered plants be multiplied?

Part E: Growing and Monitoring the Cultures

20. Place both dishes under lights in the place provided by your teacher.

21. Check the dishes after a few days for evidence of growth. Any dishes with fuzzy or slimy growth visible on them have been contaminated by fungi or bacteria and should be discarded as directed by your teacher.

22. Continue to check the dishes once a week for at least five weeks and record your observations each time.

DATA AND ANALYSIS

Each week when you observe your petri dishes, record the date and dish number and draw a sketch of what you see, using a circle like the one shown below to represent the perimeter of the petri dish.

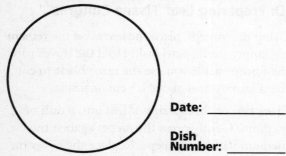

Date: _____

Dish
Number: _____

1. Why is it crucial to maintain aseptic conditions when carrying out micropropagation of plants? What is likely to happen if aseptic conditions are not maintained?

   _____

   _____

   _____

2. Explain the role that plant micropropagation plays in genetic engineering.

   _____

   _____

   _____

3. How is it possible to regenerate a new plant, with all its different tissues and organs, from just a tiny piece of leaf tissue?

   _____

   _____

   _____

4. Micropropagation is used by plant breeders and growers as well as researchers. What do you think its commercial advantages are over conventional methods of plant propagation, such as stem cuttings?

   _____

   _____

   _____

 **Pre-AP**   **Making Test Crosses**

How do breeders know the genotypes of the animals they are breeding? A test cross is one method of determining the genotype of an organism. A test cross is the mating of an individual of unknown genotype with an individual of known genotype, usually homozygous recessive. From the phenotypes of the offspring, breeders can determine the genotype of the unknown parent. In this exploration, you will be working with the fruit fly, *Drosophila melanogaster*. This species has been used extensively in the study of genetics and inheritance. These fruit flies are ideal for research because they are easily handled, they produce many offspring in a short time, they have few chromosomes, and they have many mutations that can be observed.

OBJECTIVES

In this investigation, you will

- learn to care for and raise two generations of fruit flies.

- perform two test crosses with fruit flies.

- observe the phenotypic results of the two test crosses.

- infer the genotypes of the parental fruit flies and their offspring.

- construct Punnett squares for two test crosses.

MATERIALS

culture vials with
  medium and foam
  plugs (2)
culture of vestigial-
  winged fruit flies

culture of normal-
  winged fruit flies
vial of alcohol
  anesthetic

anesthetic wand
white index card
fine-tipped paintbrush
wax pencil

stereomicroscope or
  hand lens

PROCEDURE

Part A: Test Cross 1

Use Figure 1 to identify the sexes of fruit flies. The dark, blunt abdomen with dark-colored claspers on the underside identifies the male. Males also have a pair of sex combs on the front pair of legs.

Use Figure 2 to identify a recessive trait, vestigial wings. Normal long wings (*W*) are dominant to vestigial short wings (*w*). Normal long wings enable fruit flies to fly, whereas fruit flies with vestigial short wings are unable to do so.

Figure 1

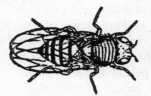

Female   Male
Sex combs

Figure 2

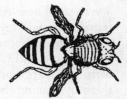

Normal wings (*W*)   Vestigial wings (*w*)

Making Test Crosses

PROCEDURE continued

1. When larvae in the normal-winged culture and the vestigial-winged culture begin to form pupae, remove all adult fruit flies from both parental cultures by anesthetizing them. To anesthetize the flies, tap each vial against a table so that the flies fall to the bottom of the vial. Quickly remove the plug and place a wand containing a few drops of anesthetic into the vial. When the flies are anesthetized, remove the wand from the vial. Place the adult flies in a vial of alcohol to kill them. This step will ensure that only virgin (unmated) females remain in the culture. Virgin female flies must be used for these test crosses to ensure that only the chosen males contribute sperm to the offspring of the cross. A female fruit fly can fertilize all the eggs she produces in her lifetime from stored sperm from a single mating. **CAUTION:** *Be careful not to spill alcohol on your clothing or to get it in your eyes. In case of spills, clean up immediately and wash your hands. Do not use alcohol near open flames.*

2. On the first morning that new adults emerge in the parental cultures, obtain a new culture vial. Label this vial "TC$_1$—female vestigial × male normal" and add your name.

3. Anesthetize and collect five virgin females from the vial of vestigial-winged flies, as well as five males from the vial of normal-winged flies. Use a stereomicroscope or hand lens to aid in identification of males and females. Use a paintbrush to pick up and move the flies. Place a white index card under the flies as a background for easier observation. Act carefully but quickly, before the anesthetic wears off.

4. Place the ten flies into the vial marked "TC$_1$" and plug the vial with a foam plug. **HINT:** *To ensure that the flies are not harmed, always leave the vial on its side until the flies recover from the effects of the anesthetic.* These ten parental flies will mate, the female flies will lay eggs, and larvae will appear in 8 to 10 days. These offspring are the results of the first test cross (TC$_1$). When the larvae begin to form pupae, remove the parental flies and kill them by placing them in the vial of alcohol.

5. Record the numbers and types of parental flies in Table 1.

6. Store your TC$_1$ vial according to your teacher's instructions.

7. As the new TC$_1$ adults emerge over a period of about two weeks, anesthetize and count the numbers and types of flies that appear in this TC$_1$ generation. Record these data in Table 1. You may wish to carry out Part B, steps 1 and 2 as you work on this step.

Part B: Test Cross 2

1. Label a new culture vial "TC$_2$—female vestigial × male TC$_1$," and add your name.

2. As you anesthetize and count TC$_1$ adults from Part A, place five male TC$_1$ adults into the TC$_2$ vial.

3. Collect five virgin females from the original culture of vestigial-winged fruit flies. Place these in the TC$_2$ vial with the five males. These ten fruit flies will be used in the second text cross.

4. Record the numbers and types of parental flies in Table 2.

5. When larvae begin to appear in the TC$_2$ vial, remove the adult flies and kill them in the vial of alcohol. Do not add any more flies to the TC$_2$ vial.

6. As TC$_2$ adults emerge from their pupae, anesthetize and count the different types of flies. Remove flies to the vial of alcohol after they have been counted.

7. Record your data for the TC$_2$ generation in Table 2.

8. Store or dispose of your cultures as directed by your teacher.

Making Test Crosses

DATA AND ANALYSIS

Table 1 Test Cross 1

Generation	Number of Flies of Each Wing Type	
	Normal-winged	Vestigial-winged
Parental males		
Parental females		
TC_1 males		
TC_1 females		

Table 2 Test Cross 2

Generation	Number of Flies of Each Wing Type	
	Normal-winged	Vestigial-winged
TC_1 males		
Vestigial females		
TC_2 males		
TC_2 females		

1. What were the genotypes of the male and female parental flies from the original cultures? Explain.

_____

_____

_____

2. What were the phenotypes of the offspring flies in the TC_1 generation?

_____

3. What was the genotype of the offspring flies in the TC_1 generation? Explain.

_____

_____

_____

Making Test Crosses

DATA AND ANALYSIS continued

4. Use your answers from Analysis questions 1 and 3 to construct a Punnett square for Test Cross 1.

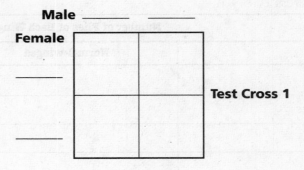

5. What were the genotypes of the male and female parent flies used in Test Cross 2?

_____

6. What were the phenotypes of the flies in the TC$_2$ offspring?

_____

_____

7. What were the genotypes of the offspring in the TC$_2$ vial? Explain.

_____

_____

_____

8. Use your answers from Analysis questions 5 and 7 to construct a Punnett square for Test Cross 2.

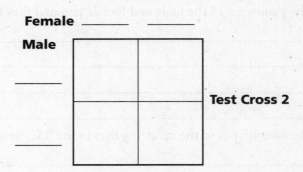

9. Based on Punnett square 2, what was the expected TC$_2$ phenotypic ratio? What was the actual TC$_2$ phenotypic ratio observed?

_____

_____

Lab

11

How is camouflage an adaptive advantage?

Natural selection can be described as the process by which those organisms best adapted to the environment are more likely to survive and reproduce than are those organisms that are poorly adapted. Organisms have developed many different kinds of adaptations that help them survive in their environments. These include adaptations for finding food, such as keen night vision in nocturnal animals, as well as adaptations for avoiding predators. Some organisms use camouflage as a way to escape predation from other organisms. Camouflage allows them to blend in with the background.

OBJECTIVES

In this investigation, you will

- use an artificial environment to model the concept of natural selection.
- hypothesize what will happen if natural selection acts over time on organisms exhibiting camouflage.

- construct bar graphs to show the results of the Investigation.
- compare the model of natural selection in the Investigation to real examples of natural selection.

MATERIALS

hole punch
colored paper (1 sheet each of purple, brown, blue, green, tan, black, orange, red, yellow, and white)
plastic film canisters or petri dishes (10)

piece of brightly colored, floral fabric (80 cm × 80 cm)
graph paper (2 sheets)

PROCEDURE

1. Work in a group of four students.
2. Punch 20 dots from each sheet of colored paper and place each color dot in a different plastic container.
3. Spread out the floral cloth on a flat surface.
4. Spread 10 dots of each color randomly over the cloth. See Figure 1.
5. Select a student to choose dots. That student must look away from the cloth, turn back to it, and then immediately pick up the first dot he or she sees.
6. Repeat step 5 until 10 dots have been picked up. Be sure the student looks away before a selection is made each time.
7. Record the results in Table 1. Return the 10 collected dots to the cloth in a random manner.

Figure 1

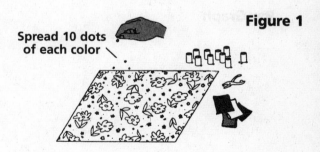

Spread 10 dots of each color

Assume that the dots represent individual organisms that, if allowed, will reproduce more of their own type (color). Also assume that the selection of dots represents predation.

8. Write a hypothesis to predict what will happen over time if selected dots are not returned to the cloth and the remaining dots "reproduce." Write your hypothesis in the space provided.

How is camouflage an adaptive advantage? **35**

Lab 11

How is camouflage an adaptive advantage?

PROCEDURE continued

9. Each student in the group must, in turn, pick up 20 dots following the method in steps 5 and 6. Place the dots in their original containers. Remember to look away each time before making a selection.

10. After each student has removed 20 dots, shake the remaining 20 dots off the cloth onto the table. See Figure 2.

11. Count and record in Table 2 the number of dots of each color that remains.

12. Give each of the "surviving" dots four "offspring" of the same color by adding dots from the containers. You may need to punch out more of certain colors. Return all of the dots to the cloth in a random manner. This will bring the total number of dots on the cloth back to 100. See Figure 3.

13. Repeat steps 9–12 three more times. Each repetition represents the survival and reproduction of a single generation. Continue to record the results of each repetition in Table 2.

14. Make a bar graph in the space below to show the number of dots of each color that were on the cloth at the beginning of the Investigation. Label the horizontal axis with the names of the 10 colors and the vertical axis with the number of dots.

Bar Graph

15. Make a second bar graph in the space to the right to show the number of dots of each color that were on the cloth at the end of the fourth generation. Label the axes as on the first graph.

Figure 2

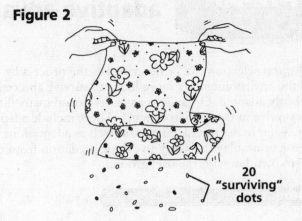

20 "surviving" dots

Figure 3

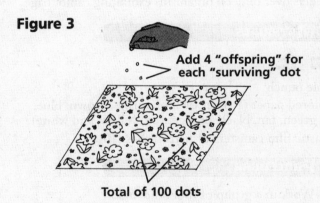

Add 4 "offspring" for each "surviving" dot

Total of 100 dots

Bar Graph

Lab 11

How is camouflage an adaptive advantage?

DATA AND ANALYSIS

Table 1

Selection of Dots	
Color	Number of dots selected
Purple	
Brown	
Blue	
Green	
Tan	
Black	
Orange	
Red	
Yellow	
White	

Table 2

	Number of Dots Remaining After Each Generation			
	Number remaining after generation			
Color	1	2	3	4
Purple				
Brown				
Blue				
Green				
Tan				
Black				
Orange				
Red				
Yellow				
White				

1. Hypothesis

_____

_____

_____

2. Which colors were picked up from the floral background?

_____

_____

3. Which colors, if any, were not picked up? Why not?

_____

_____

4. If the dots represent food to a predator, what is the advantage of being a color that blends in with the background?

_____

_____

How is camouflage an adaptive advantage?

DATA AND ANALYSIS continued

5. Give two examples of real organisms that use camouflage to avoid predation.

_____

_____

6. As the dots on the cloth passed through several generations, what trends in frequency of colors did you observe?

_____

_____

7. How would the outcome of this Investigation have differed if the "predator" was color-blind? Explain.

_____

_____

8. How would the outcome of this Investigation have been affected if dots that were subject to predation (those picked up) tasted bad or were able to harm the predator in some way, such as by stinging it?

_____

_____

_____

9. Describe an example of natural selection that is similar to the model of natural selection in this Investigation.

_____

_____

10. Was your hypothesis supported by your data? Why or why not?

_____

_____

Pre-AP | Biochemical Evidence for Evolution

If two organisms have similar DNA molecules, they have similar proteins. Similar proteins have similar amino acid sequences (orders). Thus, if amino acid sequences are similar, DNA of the organisms is similar.

Some scientists believe that similar DNA sequences indicate a common origin. The more similar the DNA of two living organisms, the more closely related they may be to one another.

Hemoglobin, a protein in red blood cells, has been studied. Scientists know the specific amino acids and their arrangements in hemoglobin molecules of humans, gorillas, and horses.

OBJECTIVES

In this investigation, you will

- count and record differences in the sequence of amino acids in similar portions of human, gorilla, and horse hemoglobin.

- count and record the molecules of each amino acid present in similar portions of human, gorilla, and horse hemoglobin.

- use these data to show how biochemical evidence can be used to support evolution.

PROCEDURE

Part A: Amino Acid Sequence

Figure 2 on page 40 represents the amino acid sequence of corresponding portions of the hemoglobin molecules of horses, gorillas, and humans.

1. Read the amino acid sequences from left to right beginning at the upper left-hand corner of Figure 2. Compare the sequences of humans to the sequences of gorillas and horses. An example of a sequence difference between humans and gorillas is shown in Figure 1.

2. Record in Table 1 the total number of differences in the sequences of gorilla and human amino acids. Then repeat this procedure for horse and human, and for gorilla and horse.

Part B: Numbers of Amino Acids

1. Count the number of each kind of amino acid in human hemoglobin. Record the totals in the proper column of Table 2.

2. Count each amino acid in the hemoglobin of gorillas and horses. Record these in Table 2.

Figure 1

Human:	Val	His	Pro
Gorilla:	Val	His	Gly
Horse:	Val	His	Pro

This is a sequence difference between human and gorilla.

This is a sequence difference between gorilla and horse.

This is not a sequence difference between human and horse.

Biochemical Evidence for Evolution

Figure 2

Human:	Val	His	Leu	Thr	Pro	Glu	Glu	Lys	Ser	Ala	Val	Thr	Ala	Leu	Try
Gorilla:	Val	His	Leu	Thr	Pro	Glu	Glu	Lys	Ser	Ala	Val	Thr	Ala	Leu	Try
Horse:	Val	Glu	Leu	Ser	Gly	Glu	Glu	Lys	Ala	A)a	Val	Leu	Ala	Leu	Try

Human:	Gly	Lys	Val	Asp	Val	Asp	Glu	Val	Gly	Gly	Glu	Ala	Leu	Gly	Arg
Gorilla:	Gly	Lys	Val	Asp	Val	Asp	Glu	Val	Gly	Gly	Glu	Ala	Leu	Gly	Arg
Horse:	Asp	Lys	Val	Asp	Glu	Glu	Glu	Val	Gly	Gly	Glu	Ala	Leu	Gly	Arg

Human:	Leu	Leu	Val	Val	Tyr	Pro	Try	Thr	Glu	Arg	Phe	Phe	Glu	Ser	Phe
Gorilla:	Leu	Leu	Val	Val	Tyr	Pro	Try	Thr	Glu	Arg	Phe	Phe	Glu	Ser	Phe
Horse:	Leu	Leu	Val	Val	Tyr	Pro	Try	Thr	Glu	Arg	Phe	Phe	Asp	Ser	Phe

Human:	Gly	Asp	Leu	Ser	Thr	Pro	Asp	Ala	Val	Met	Gly	Asp	Pro	Lys	Val
Gorilla:	Gly	Asp	Leu	Ser	Thr	Pro	Asp	Ala	Val	Met	Gly	Asp	Pro	Lys	Val
Horse:	Gly	Asp	Leu	Ser	Asp	Pro	Gly	Ala	Val	Met	Gly	Asp	Pro	Lys	Val

Human:	Lys	Ala	His	Gly	Lys	Lys	Val	Leu	Gly	Ala	Phe	Ser	Asp	Gly	Leu
Gorilla:	Lys	Ala	His	Gly	Lys	Lys	Val	Leu	Gly	Ala	Phe	Ser	Asp	Gly	Leu
Horse:	Lys	Ala	His	Gly	Lys	Lys	Val	Leu	His	Ser	Phe	Gly	Giu	Gly	Val

Human:	Ala	His	Leu	Asp	Asp	Leu	Lys	Gly	Thr	Phe	Ala	Thr	Leu	Ser	Glu
Gorilla:	Ala	His	Leu	Asp	Asp	Leu	Lys	Gly	Thr	Phe	Ala	Thr	Leu	Ser	Glu
Horse:	His	His	Leu	Asp	Asp	Leu	Lys	Gly	Thr	Phe	Ala	Ala	Leu	Ser	Glu

Human:	Leu	His	Cys	Asp	Lys	Leu	His	Val	Asp	Pro	Glu	Asp	Phe	Arg	Leu
Gorilla:	Leu	His	Cys	Asp	Lys	Leu	His	Val	Asp	Pro	Glu	Asp	Phe	Leu	Leu
Horse:	Leu	His	Cys	Asp	Lys	Leu	His	Val	Asp	Pro	Glu	Asp	Phe	Arg	Leu

Human:	Leu	Gly	Asp	Val	Leu	Val	Cys	Val	Leu	Ala	His	His	Phe	Gly	Lys
Gorilla:	Leu	Gly	Asp	Val	Leu	Val	Cys	Val	Leu	Ala	His	His	Phe	Gly	Lys
Horse:	Leu	Gly	Asp	Val	Leu	Ala	Leu	Val	Val	Ala	Arg	His	Phe	Gly	Lys

Human:	Glu	Phe	Thr	Pro	Pro	Val	Glu	Ala	Ala	Tyr	Glu	Lys	Val	Val	Ala
Gorilla:	Glu	Phe	Thr	Pro	Pro	Val	Glu	Ala	Ala	Tyr	Glu	Lys	Val	Val	Ala
Horse:	Asp	Phe	Thr	Pro	Glu	Leu	Glu	Ala	Ser	Tyr	Glu	Lys	Val	Val	Ala

Human:	Gly	Val	Ala	Asp	Ala	Leu	Ala	His	Lys	Tyr	His
Gorilla:	Gly	Val	Ala	Asp	Ala	Leu	Ala	His	Lys	Tyr	His
Horse:	Gly	Val	Ala	Asp	Ala	Leu	Ala	His	Lys	Tyr	His

Biochemical Evidence for Evolution

DATA AND ANALYSIS

Table 1

Organisms	Number of Amino Acid Sequence Differences	
	Number of Differences	
Gorilla and human		
Horse and human		
Gorilla and horse		

Table 2

		Number of Each Amino Acid		
Amino Acid	**Abbreviation**	**Human**	**Gorilla**	**Horse**
Alanine	Ala			
Arginine	Arg			
Aspartic acid	Asp			
Cysteine	Cys			
Glutamic acid	Glu			
Glycine	Gly			
Histidine	His			
Leucine	Leu			
Lysine	Lys			
Methionine	Met			
Phenylalanine	Phe			
Proline	Pro			
Serine	Ser			
Threonine	Thr			
Tryptophan	Try			
Tyrosine	Tyr			
Valine	Val			

Biochemical Evidence for Evolution

DATA AND ANALYSIS continued

1. Where is hemoglobin normally found? _____

2. How many different kinds of amino acids are present in these three animals' hemoglobin? _____

3. (a) Which amino acid is most common in all three animals? _____

   (b) Which amino acid is the least common in all three animals? _____

4. Use your data from Table 1 to answer these questions.
   (a) How similar are the ammo acid sequences of human and gorilla hemoglobin? _____

   (b) How similar are human and horse hemoglobin? _____

   (c) How similar are gorilla and horse hemoglobin? _____

5. Of the different types of amino acids found in hemoglobin,
   (a) how many are present in the same exact number in humans and gorillas? _____

   (b) in humans and horses? _____

   (c) in gorillas and horses? _____

6. On the basis of your answer to question 5,
   (a) how similar are the chemical makeups of human and gorilla hemoglobin? _____

   (b) how similar are human and horse hemoglobin? _____

   (c) how similar are gorilla and horse hemoglobin? _____

7. Which two animals seem to have more similar hemoglobin? _____

8. In numbers, explain how the base sequences (genes) for hemoglobin formation on human chromosomes differ from those in gorillas. (How many bases are different?) _____

9. Give reasons for supporting or rejecting the following statement. Upon examination, segments of human and gorilla DNA responsible for inheritance of hemoglobin should appear almost chemically alike. _____

   _____

   _____

   _____

10. Give reasons for supporting or rejecting the following statement. Evolutionary relationships are stronger between living organisms which have close biochemical (protein) similarities than between living organisms which do not have close biochemical similarities. _____

   _____

   _____

   _____

Pre-AP Transpiration in Plants

Water is absorbed through the root system of higher plants and carried upward through the stem to the leaves. Water is used chiefly in the process of photosynthesis; however, a large amount of the moved water is lost by transpiration. Transpiration is a process in which water evaporates through leaves. A corn plant transpires about 190 liters of water during a 100-day growing season. Transpiration is partially responsible for water movement from roots to leaves in a plant. A potometer is an instrument used to determine water loss by transpiration.

Water molecules have strong attractive forces which hold the molecules together. These forces cause water to exist as continuous columns from roots to leaves in a plant. As water evaporates from a leaf, the protoplasm begins to dry slightly. The drying protoplasm attracts water from other nearby cells that have a higher water content. These cells in turn attract water from the xylem vessels in the leaf. The leaf xylem attracts water from the stem xylem which attracts water from the root xylem. The root xylem attracts water from the surrounding cortex cells. Cortex receives water from the epidermal cells of the root.

OBJECTIVES

In this investigation, you will
- assemble a potometer
- determine the rate of transpiration in a given plant species
- determine the effect of certain environmental factors on transpiration rate

Figure 1

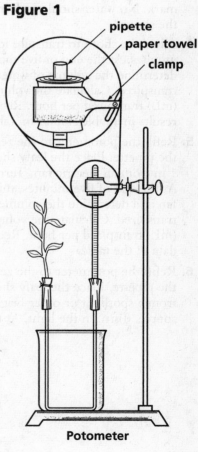

pipette
paper towel
clamp

Potometer

MATERIALS

burner
iron stand
test tube clamp
glass tubing (20 cm)
rubber tubing (two 6-cm sections)
beaker (1000-mL)
paper toweling
water
beaker large enough to hold the "U" tube

5-mL pipettes (2)
cord (10 cm)
razor blade or scalpel
potted plant
electric fan
spotlight or other bright light
petroleum jelly

PROCEDURE

1. Set up a potometer as shown in Figure 1. Make a cylinder out of a paper towel to cushion the pipette from the clamp. Insert the pipette through the cylinder, and fasten the test tube clamp firmly around the paper toweling. Mount the clamp and pipette on the iron stand. Heat a piece of glass tubing with the flame of a burner and bend it in the form of a "U." Attach the "U" tube to the 5-mL pipette with a six-centimeter length of rubber tubing. Make sure the rubber tubing fits snugly on the pipette and "U" tube. Insert another six-centimeter length of tubing on the other end of the "U" tube. Set the "U" tube in a beaker.

Transpiration in Plants

PROCEDURE continued

2. With a razor blade or scalpel, remove a leafy shoot from a potted plant. Place the shoot in a large beaker of water. Holding the cut end under water, cut off a 2 to 3 cm section from the cut end of the plant to remove any air in the xylem vessels. Keep the shoot submerged in the beaker.

3. With another pipette, fill the potometer by adding water to the pipette attached to the potometer. Add water until it overflows from the other side of the "U." When overflowing occurs, insert the leafy shoot into the rubber tubing. Tie the cord as tight as possible around the rubber tubing holding the shoot. Fill the pipette part of the potometer to the zero mark. No water should leak from around the shoot.

4. Allow the shoot to transpire for five minutes. At the end of five minutes, determine the volume of water that has transpired. Calculate the volume of water (mL) transpired per hour. Record your results in a table similar to Table 1.

5. Refill the potometer to the zero mark of the pipette. Place the leafy shoot about 1 m from an electric fan. Turn on the fan. At the end of five minutes, turn off the fan and determine the volume of water transpired. Calculate the volume of water (mL) transpired per hour. Record the data in the table.

6. Refill the potometer to the zero mark of the pipette. Place the leafy shoot 1 m from a spotlight or other bright light source. Turn on the light. At the end of

five minutes, turn off the light and determine the volume of water transpired. Calculate the volume of water (mL) transpired per hour. Record the data in the table.

7. Refill the potometer to the zero mark of the pipette. Coat the upper surface of all leaves of the shoot with petroleum jelly. Place the leafy shoot 1 m from the electric fan. Turn on the fan. At the end of five minutes, turn off the fan and determine the volume of water transpired. Calculate the volume of water (mL) transpired per hour. Record the data in the table.

8. Refill the potometer to the zero mark of the pipette. Coat the lower surface of the leaves of the shoot with petroleum jelly. Do not remove the petroleum jelly from the upper surface of the leaves. Place the leafy shoot 1 m from the electric fan. Turn on the fan. At the end of five minutes, turn off the fan and determine the volume of water transpired. Calculate the volume of water (mL) transpired per hour. Record the data in the table.

9. Collect class data for each species of plant used of the volume of water transpired per hour. Record the class data in a table similar to Table 2.

Transpiration in Plants

DATA AND ANALYSIS

Table 1

Individual Data on Amount of Water Transpired			
Condition	Plant Used	mL of Water Transpired	mL of Water Transpired Per Hour
Normal			
Fan			
Spotlight			
Petroleum jelly (upper surface)			
Petroleum jelly (both surfaces)			

Table 2

Type of Plant	Class Data on Amount of Water Transpired				
	mL of Water Transpired Per Hour				
	Normal	Fan	Spotlight	Petroleum Jelly (Upper Surface)	Petroleum Jelly (Both Surfaces)
Coleus					
Geranium					

1. What environmental factors did you use that increased the rate of transpiration?

2. What environmental factors did you not use that would increase the rate of transpiration?

3. What environmental factors did you use that decreased the rate of transpiration?

4. What effect would the size of the leaf have on the rate of transpiration?

5. What other factors affect the rate of transpiration?

Transpiration in Plants

DATA AND ANALYSIS continued

6. How do the fan, spotlight, and petroleum jelly increase or decrease the transpiration rate?

_____

7. Did any of the three conditions (fan, spotlight, or petroleum jelly) increase or decrease the rate of transpiration more than the others? Explain.

_____

_____

_____

8. From the class data arrange in order from the greatest to the least the transpiration rate in the various species of plants.

_____

_____

9. Why do you think each species of plant transpires at a different rate?

_____

10. Were any controls used in this investigation?

_____

11. If you were to do this investigation again, what factors would you be certain to control?

_____

_____

12. How did these factors affect your results?

_____

_____

Pre-AP   The Human Heart

Heart muscle tissue contracts and relaxes to pump blood throughout your body. The blood, carrying oxygen and other materials, moves through the circulatory system which is composed of arteries, capillaries, and veins.

OBJECTIVES

In this investigation, you will
- follow the pathway of blood through the heart.
- determine the amount of oxygen or carbon dioxide contained in blood in each side of the heart.

- follow the sequence of events occurring as a heart beats.
- measure blood pressure differences in arteries and veins using a heart-blood vessel model.

MATERIALS

plastic bottle
2-hole stopper to fit bottle
metric ruler
glass tube, 3 cm long
glass tube, 18 cm long
plastic tube, 15 cm long

PROCEDURE

Part A: Heart Anatomy and Blood Flow

Study Figure 1 to determine the names and locations of all major blood vessels and heart structures. This diagram is a front view of the heart, which makes the labels indicating left and right sides appear to be reversed. All shaded areas are muscle. Unshaded areas are filled with blood.

1. Complete Table 1 indicating the direction of blood flow.

    (a) Blood moves to two organs from the right side of the heart. What are these organs?_____
    _____

    (b) Blood is received from two organs on the left side of the heart. What are these organs?_____
    _____

Part B: Condition of Blood as It Flows Through the Heart

All vessels bringing blood to the heart's right side and leaving from the right ventricle, contain blood that is deoxygenated. Deoxygenated blood is low in oxygen and high in carbon dioxide.

All vessels bringing blood to the heart's left side and leaving from the left ventricle contain oxygenated blood. Oxygenated blood is high in oxygen and low in carbon dioxide.

2. Complete Table 2 indicating the oxygen content of blood. Use the terms "deoxygenated" and "oxygenated." Refer to Figure 1 for help.

    (a) Describe the condition of blood in all parts of the right side of the heart. _____

    (b) Describe the condition of blood in all parts of the left side of the heart. _____

The Human Heart

PROCEDURE continued

Figure 1

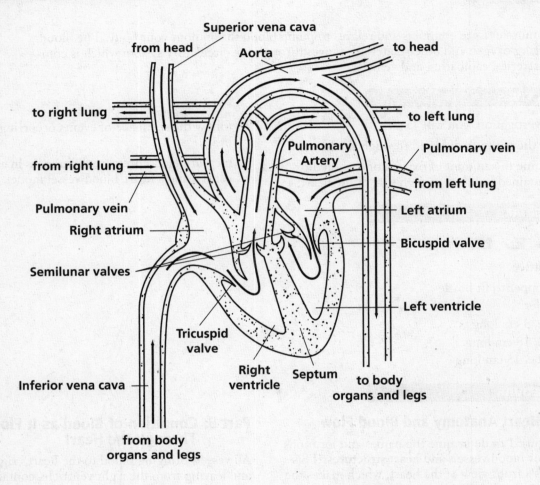

from head
Superior vena cava
Aorta
to head

to right lung
to left lung

Pulmonary
Artery
Pulmonary vein

from right lung
from left lung

Pulmonary vein
Left atrium

Right atrium
Bicuspid valve

Semilunar valves
Left ventricle

Tricuspid
valve

Inferior vena cava
Right
ventricle
Septum
to body
organs and legs

from body
organs and legs

RIGHT
LEFT

Lab

The Human Heart

14

Part C: Heart Pumping Action

In order to move blood through the heart, a pumping action must occur. It is the ventricles that aid in the pumping action of the heart. Heart valves keep the blood flowing in one direction as the ventricles squeeze or pump blood through the heart.

1. Examine Figure 2 showing the ventricles relaxed and not pumping blood. This relaxed condition is called diastole.

2. Complete the left column of Table 3 while looking at Figure 2.

3. Examine Figure 3 showing the ventricle sides pushing in and squeezing and pumping blood out of the heart. This pumping action is called systole.

4. Complete the right column of Table 3 by looking at Figure 3.

   (a) During diastole, are the ventricles filling or being emptied of blood?_____

   (b) During systole, are the ventricles filling or being emptied of blood?_____

A continuous pattern of diastole and systole allows the heart to pump blood to all parts of the body. The heart relaxes and fills with blood, then pumps. It relaxes again while it refills, and then pumps again. You detect this pattern of relaxing and pumping when you feel your pulse.

Figure 2

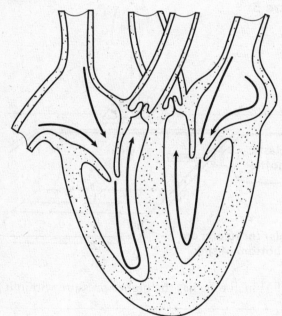

Figure 3

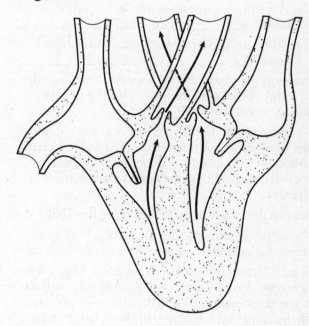

The Human Heart

Part D: Blood Pressure Model

Blood is under pressure as the heart pumps it through your body. The amount of pressure, however, varies throughout your body. Blood vessels called arteries have thicker walls and are less flexible. Arteries have blood under high pressure. Other blood vessels, veins, have blood under low pressure because of their thinner, more flexible walls and because of the loss of pressure that occurs as blood passes through the capillaries.

1. Secure a plastic bottle from your teacher.

2. Fill it with water and seal it with the provided rubber stopper and tube assembly. The finished apparatus should look like Figure 4. Note that one of the tubes leading from the stopper is glass while the other is plastic.

   (a) Which tube represents the flexible blood vessel? _____

   (b) Which tube represents the inflexible blood vessel? _____

3. Position the plastic bottle assembly near the edge of a sink. Place a metric ruler into the sink as shown in Figure 5.

4. Give the plastic bottle one firm squeeze. Measure the distance in millimeters that the water streams shoot out of the ends of the tubes. It is best to measure where the streams strike the bottom of the sink.

5. Record the distances in Table 4 using the Trial 1 row.

6. Repeat the squeezing and measuring four more times. Calculate an average distance for each tube.

   A tube having more flexible sides will have a lower pressure. A tube having less flexible sides will have a greater pressure. The higher the pressure, the farther a stream of water will shoot from a tube. The lower the pressure, the shorter a stream of water will shoot from a tube.

   (a) Which tube has the longer average stream of water? _____

   (b) Which tube has the shorter average stream of water? _____

Figure 4

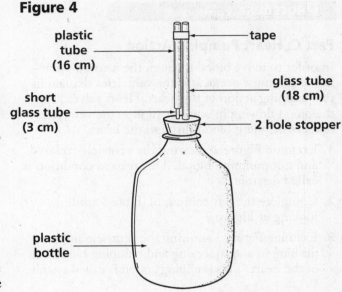

plastic tube (16 cm)   tape
short glass tube (3 cm)   glass tube (18 cm)
2 hole stopper
plastic bottle

Figure 5

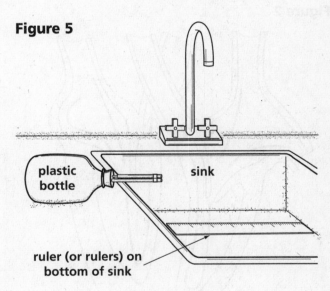

plastic bottle   sink
ruler (or rulers) on bottom of sink

(c) Which tube has the higher pressure within it?

_____

(d) Which tube has the lower pressure within it?

_____

(e) Which tube represented an artery?

_____

(f) Which tube represented a vein?

_____

The Human Heart

DATA AND ANALYSIS

Table 1

Blood Flow		
Receives Blood from		
Left side	1.	
	2.	
Right side	1.	
	2.	
Pumps Blood to		
Left side	1.	
	2.	
Right side	1.	
	2.	

Table 2

Oxygen Content of Blood	
Chamber or Vessel	**Oxygenated or Deoxygenated**
Left ventricle	
Right ventricle	
Left atrium	
Right atrium	
Pulmonary artery	
Pulmonary vein	
Superior vena cava	
Inferior vena cava	
Aorta	

1. Define the following terms:

   (a) oxygenated blood _____

   (b) deoxygenated blood _____

   (c) systole _____

   (d) diastole _____

2. Blood is changed from an oxygenated to a deoxygenated condition or vice versa in the circulatory system.

   Which change occurs in lung capillaries? _____

   Which change occurs in body capillaries? _____

3. Using Figure 1 as a guide, tell where blood goes when it leaves the

   (a) aorta. _____

   (b) pulmonary artery. _____

   (c) right and left atria. _____

4. Using Figure 1 as a guide, tell where blood comes from in each of the following structures.

   (a) superior vena cava _____

   (b) inferior vena cava _____

   (c) pulmonary vein _____

5. Describe the direction of blood flow through the right side of the heart. Include the names of all blood vessels leading into and out of the right side as well as valves involved in blood flow. Indicate which chambers are in systole and diastole. _____

_____

_____

The Human Heart

DATA AND ANALYSIS continued

Table 3

	Ventricles in	
	Diastole	**Systole**
Relaxed or pumping		
Bi- and tricuspid valves open or closed?*		
Blood flowing past bi- and tricuspid valves?		
Blood flowing into ventricles from atria?		
Semilunar valves open or closed?*		
Blood flowing past semilunar valves?		
Blood flowing out of ventricles into aorta or pulmonary artery?		
*Valves are open if their tips are not touching.		

Table 4

	Experimental Results	
	Glass Tube	**Plastic Tube**
Trial 1		
Trial 2		
Trial 3		
Trial 4		
Trial 5		
Totals		
Average distance		

6. Describe the direction of blood flow through the left side of the heart in the same way as in question 5.

_____

_____

7. Your heart ejects or pumps about 60 mL of blood into the aorta each time it undergoes systole.

(a) How many times in one minute does your heart pump (beat)? _____

(b) Calculate the amount of blood pumped by your heart in one minute. _____

8. (a) Assume that the bi-and tricuspid valves were closed during diastole. What would happen to blood movement? _____

(b) Assume that the semilunar valves were closed during systole. What would happen to blood movement? _____

Lab

The Human Heart

14

9. In Part D, what body part was represented by the

 (a) plastic bottle? _____

 (b) water in the bottle? _____

 (c) plastic tube? _____

 (d) glass tube? _____

10. A student observes the following cross section slices of blood vessels under the microscope.

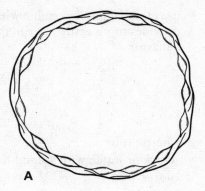 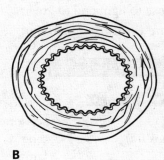

A   B

 (a) Which vessel is probably an artery? _____
 Why? _____
 _____
 _____

 (b) Which vessel is probably a vein? _____
 Why? _____
 _____
 _____

Pre-AP   Earthworm Behavior

An organism responds to changes in its environment. Biologists refer to these responses as behavior. Behavior may be of two types: unlearned (innate) behavior, or learned (modified) behavior.

OBJECTIVES

In this investigation, you will

- conduct experiments that will show earthworms' unlearned response to light and to gravity.
- observe and record earthworm behavior.

- contribute your data to class totals.
- use class data to determine which experiment provides more easily interpretable earthworm behavior.

MATERIALS

live earthworms   scissors   metric ruler
shoe box (or shoe box lid)   tape   clock or watch with second hand
paper towels   lamp   water
black paper   cardboard

PROCEDURE

Part A: Response to Light

1. Prepare an experimental chamber for earthworms by taping black paper over one-half of a shoe box (Figure 1).

2. Position a lamp above the chamber so that the light shines directly on it.

3. Place wet paper towels in the shoe box.

4. Place two (or more if available) earthworms in the chamber so that their anterior ends are in the light and their posterior ends are under the paper screen. NOTE: The anterior end of a worm is closest to the bandlike structure (clitellum). This band appears orange-brown on live animals.

5. Wait five minutes. Then record in Table 1 the number of worms whose anterior ends are still in the light and the number of worms whose anterior ends are now under the paper screen (in the dark).

6. Repeat this procedure for four more trials. Reposition all worms with their anterior ends in the light at the start of each new trial. Record your observations for each trial.

Figure 1

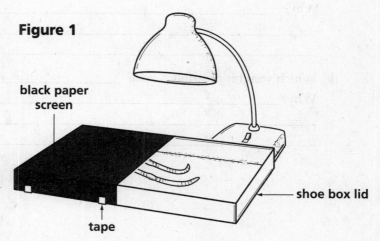

black paper screen

shoe box lid

tape

7. Repeat the entire procedure for five trials of five minutes each. However, now position the worms so that anterior ends are placed under the paper screen and posterior ends are in the light at the start of each new trial.

Earthworm Behavior

PROCEDURE continued

8. Record your observations for each trial in Table 1. Total all data from each column and record this number under "Individual totals."

9. Record class totals in Table 1.

Part B: Response to Gravity

1. Cut a square piece of cardboard to measure 25 cm on each side.

2. Draw a line across the middle of your cardboard.

3. With the cardboard flat on your desk, position your earthworms so that the anterior end of each worm is on the line (Figure 2).

4. Wait exactly one minute. Count the number of worms whose anterior ends have moved over the line, the number whose anterior ends have moved behind the line, and the number that have not moved at all. NOTE: If a worm turns to the side, judge its position in relation to where its anterior end lies (either in front or behind the line).

5. Record your observations in Table 2.

6. Record results for nine more one-minute trials. Remember to reposition all worms at the start of each new trial.

7. Tip your cardboard at an angle of about 10° with the table top. Support the cardboard with a book (Figure 3).

8. Position all worms so that their anterior ends are on the line and the worms are facing toward the high end of the cardboard.

9. Wait one minute. Then record in Table 2 the number of worms whose anterior ends have moved up (crossed the line), moved down, and have not moved.

10. Record in Table 2 nine more one-minute trials. Remember to reposition all worms at the start of each new trial.

Figure 2

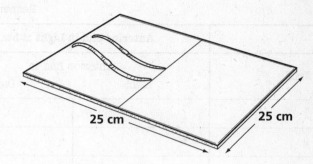

25 cm   25 cm

11. Repeat the entire procedure, using ten one-minute trials. However, now position all worms so that their anterior ends are on the line and they are facing the low end of the cardboard (Figure 4).

12. Record all results in Table 2. Total data for each column. Record this number under "Individual totals."

13. Record class totals in Table 2.

Figure 3

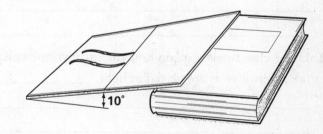

10°

Figure 4

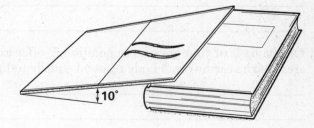

10°

Earthworm Behavior

DATA AND ANALYSIS

Table 1

Trial	Response to Light			
	Anterior End in Light at Start		**Anterior End in Dark at Start**	
	Anterior End in		Anterior End in	
	Light	Dark	Light	Dark
1				
2				
3				
4				
5				
Individual totals				
Class totals				

1. Briefly restate the specific behavior being tested in Part A of this investigation. _____
_____
_____

2. Using class totals, explain how the earthworm's behavior is influenced by light when

   (a) anterior ends are placed in light. _____
   _____
   _____

   (b) posterior ends are placed in light. _____
   _____
   _____

3. On the basis of your answers to question 2, offer experimental evidence which explains whether or not all areas of the earthworm's body respond equally to light or dark. _____
_____
_____

Earthworm Behavior

DATA AND ANALYSIS continued

4. (a) Does the earthworm's response to light have any adaptive or protective value? _____

    (b) Explain. _____

_____

5. Briefly restate the behavior being tested in Part B of this investigation. _____

_____

_____

6. Using class totals only, what conclusions may be made about the earthworm's response to gravity? (If an earthworm responds by moving toward gravity, it is positively geotactic; if it moves away from gravity, it is negatively geotactic.) _____

7. (a) If you were to choose between the experiment in Part A and the one in Part B on the basis of reliable and accurate data, which would you choose? _____

    (b) Why? _____

8. On the basis of your answer to question 7, explain why experiments on animal behavior may be difficult to conduct and interpret. _____

_____

_____

Earthworm Behavior

DATA AND ANALYSIS continued

Table 2

Response to Gravity									
	Worms Flat on Desk			Worms Facing Up Away from Gravity			Worms Facing Down Toward Gravity		
Trial	Anterior End over Line	Anterior End Behind Line	No Change	Anterior End over Line	Anterior End Behind Line	No Change	Anterior End over Line	Anterior End Behind Line	No Change
1									
2									
3									
4									
5									
6									
7									
8									
9									
10									
Individual totals									
Class totals									

Pre-AP   Field Studies of a Freshwater Ecosystem

Afreshwater stream is the habitat for many living things. Many organisms exchange gases with the water environment.

Living things are found in a freshwater stream throughout the entire year. However, the population density of each species does not remain the same all year. Changes in the chemical and physical characteristics of the stream influence what organisms will inhabit a certain area. For example, rocks, a physical factor of a stream, are habitats for many bottom-dwelling organisms. If the number of sizes of rocks change, available habitat for many bottom-dwelling organisms changes. Changes in chemical factors, such as the concentrations of oxygen and carbon dioxide, also determine what type of organism can inhabit the stream. Behavior patterns of entire communities are affected by changes in the physical and chemical environment.

OBJECTIVES

In this investigation, you will

- set up seven stations on a freshwater stream
- observe, distinguish, and record various physical factors of the stream

- observe, describe, and identify the organisms of the stream
- compare and analyze the relationship of the physical factors to the organisms from the collected data

MATERIALS

Field Materials

hammer
stakes or large nails (14)
cord (100 m)
metersticks (3)
white lid from jar
graph paper (8 sheets)
capped plastic bottle
baby food jars (3 to 4 dozen)
small jars (4)
medium jars (4)

Classroom Analysis

microscopes (3)
stereomicroscopes (3)
coverslips (3)

large jars (4)
Celsius thermometers (2)
100-mL sample bottles
   (1 to 2 dozen)
phenolphthalein (25 mL)
pipette with 0.1 mL graduations
0.4% sodium hydroxide (50 mL)
pH kit
large plastic bags (1 dozen)
household sieve, large
hand lens

glass slides (3)
hand lens
dropper

70% ethyl alcohol (4 to 6 L)
net, 1.5 × 3 m
white enamel trays, large (2)
forceps
glass marker
watch with second hand

Figure 1

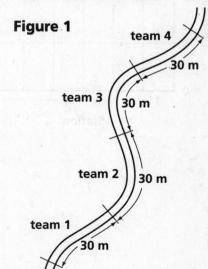

team 4
30 m
team 3
30 m
team 2
30 m
team 1
30 m

PROCEDURE

Working in teams of ten, you are to study a 30-m section of a stream. The beginning and end of your 30-m section will be the beginning or end of another team's section (Figure 1).

Field Studies of a Freshwater Ecosystem

PROCEDURE continued

Figure 2

**one-half distance from
bank to mid-channel**

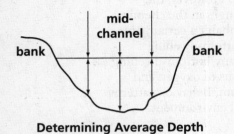

Determining Average Depth

Choose seven areas or stations for study along your team's stream section. Among these stations should be rapids, deep pools, and slow moving areas. Determine your seven stations before proceeding any further. Mark the seven areas by driving two stakes opposite one another along both banks of the stream at each station. Stretch a piece of cord from one stake to the other at each station. Do not turn over rocks on the bottom of the stream as you are setting up your stations. Disturbing rocks will interfere with certain physical and chemical samples that you are to obtain.

Part A: Physical Factors

1. Observe the bottom of the stream at each station. Record the type of bottom (substratum). Classify the bottom materials of the stream at each station as one of the following:
   (a) loose rock or gravel (easily moved)
   (b) attached rock (embedded in mud)
   (c) bedrock
   (d) sand
   (e) mud or silt
   (f) other

2. Determine the average depth and width of the stream at each station. To determine the average depth, measure the depth at three points. Measure the depth at mid-channel and at one half the distance from mid-channel to each bank (Figure 2). Record the three depths for each station in your notebook. Add the three depths and divide by four. Dividing by four compensates for the narrow depth near the banks.

Figure 3

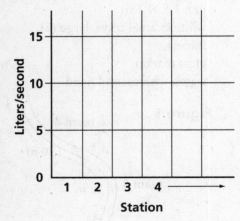

3. To determine the average width, measure the distance across the channel at three places near the station. Select areas within 3 meters of the station. If possible, select an area that is wide, one that is narrow, and one that is half-way between wide and narrow. Add the three distances and divide by three.

4. Record the average widths and depths in your notebook. Compare your averages for each station with other members of the class. Construct graphs showing the average width and depth at each station.

5. Determine the volume of flow of the stream at each station. Place a capped plastic bottle in mid-channel at a station. Record in your notebook the time (in seconds) it takes the plastic bottle to travel a measured distance. Using the following formula, calculate the volume of flow at each station in cubic meters per second:

$$R = \frac{WDaL}{T}$$

Field Studies of a Freshwater Ecosystem

PROCEDURE continued

R = volume of flow (cubic meters per second); W = average width of stream (in meters); D = average depth of stream (in meters); a = constant, for bottom type [0.9 for smooth (bedrock, sand, or silt bottom) or 0.8 for rough (gravel or rocky bottom)]; L = length of measured distance traveled by the bottle (in meters); and T = time for the bottle to travel measured distance (in seconds).

6. Calculate the volume of flow at each station in liters per second using the following formula:

$$R = \frac{WDaL}{T} \times 1000$$

7. Record the values in your lab notebook. Compare your data with other members of the class. Construct a bar graph showing the volume of flow in liters per second at each station (Figure 3).

8. Obtain a water sample from each station. Place the water in a small baby food jar. Record in your notebook the color of the water as clear, light, or dark and the station from which the sample was taken.

9. Determine the turbidity of the water at each station by placing a Secchi disc in the deeper pools. Make a Secchi disc by attaching a white jar lid to a meter stick (Figure 4). If the disc is slightly visible at a depth of 1.3 or more meters the water is clear. If the disc is slightly visible from 0.3 to 1.3 meters, the water is slightly turbid. If the disc is visible only from zero to 0.3 meters, the water is turbid. Record the turbidity at each station in your notebook. Compare your data with other members of the class.

10. Using a Celsius thermometer, determine the air temperature 0.3 meters above the water level at mid-channel of each station. Keep the thermometer shaded from direct sunlight. Determine the water temperature at each station by securing a water sample in a small jar from the surface at mid-channel. Determine the temperature. Record the temperature for each station in your notebook. Determine the temperatures (air and water) at half-hourly intervals during the study. Plot the temperatures for each station on graphs (Figure 5). Use one graph for air temperatures

Figure 4

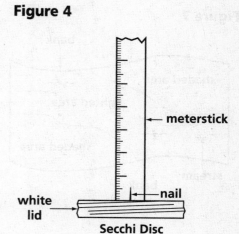

Secchi Disc

Figure 5

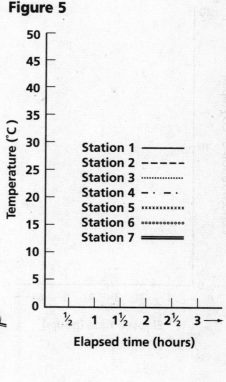

Figure 6

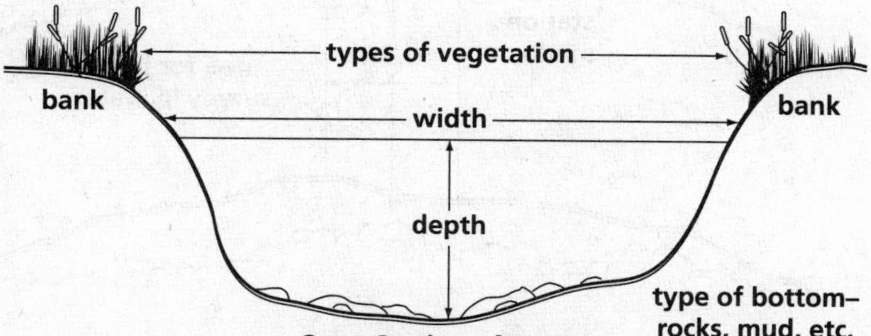

Cross-Section of Stream

Field Studies of a Freshwater Ecosystem

PROCEDURE continued

Figure 7

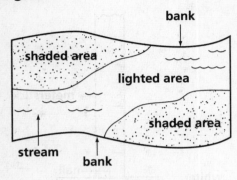

Figure 8

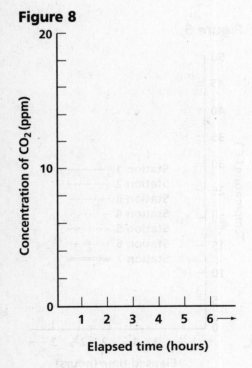

and another graph for water temperatures. Compare your data with the data of other members of the class.

11. Determine the height in meters of both banks at each station. Use the widths and depths determined earlier and the bank heights to sketch a cross section of each channel (Figure 6). Describe plant cover and soil or rock composition of banks at each station.

12. Determine the percentage of shade from overhanging trees that is present over your section of the stream. Record this data when the sun is shining. Make a drawing in your notebook similar to Figure 7. Label the parts of the stream that are shaded and lighted.

Part B: Chemical Analysis

1. To determine the amount of carbon dioxide, collect a 100-mL water sample from each station. Do not allow any air to "bubble" into the collecting jar. Add 3 drops of phenolphthalein indicator to each water sample. If the sample turns pink, pour out the contents of the collecting jar. Add water to the jar and rinse several times. Obtain another sample from the same station. Add 3 drops of phenolphthalein to the sample. With a pipette, add 0.4% sodium hydroxide solution one drop at a time until a pink color develops. Add sodium hydroxide until the pink color remains for one minute.

2. Mix the water sample after each drop of sodium hydroxide is added by swirling or rotating the container with a circular motion of the wrist. However, any agitation of the surface of the sample can add gases to the sample; therefore, avoid excessive shaking of the sample. Record the milliliters of sodium hydroxide

Figure 9

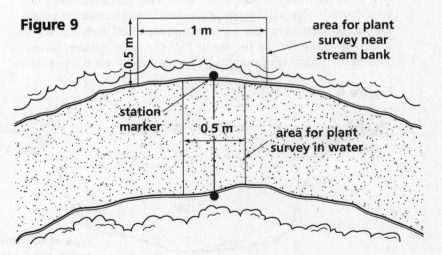

Field Studies of a Freshwater Ecosystem

PROCEDURE continued

solution used in the sample for each station. Collect a water sample every hour at each station and determine the carbon dioxide content.

3. Compute the parts per million (ppm) of carbon dioxide in the water samples from each station by multiplying the milliliters of sodium hydroxide by 100. Construct a graph showing the ppm of CO_2 at each station each hour (Figure 8).

4. Determine the pH of the water at each station at least once during the study. Place 5 mL of a water sample into a test tube. Add 3 drops of wide range pH indicator to the test tube. Cover the test tube with a rubber stopper and shake gently. Using charts with the pH kit, determine the pH of the water.

Part C: Organisms

1. Record kinds and numbers of seed plants, ferns, mosses, and/or algae growing near the edge of four stations. List the water plants as completely submerged, floating, or emergent (rooted in the bottom with stem and/or leaves above or on the surface of the water). Collect samples of each seed plant, fern, and moss. Collect one specimen of each plant type. Place the specimens in plastic bags for identification (see Figure 9).

2. Record the percentage of rocks at each station that are covered with algae. Collect samples of algae in small baby food jars for identification later.

3. Scrape debris from some rocks or decaying vegetation at each station. Place the material from each station along with 25 mL of stream water into a small baby food jar for identification later.

4. Holding a household sieve downstream from a submerged, loose rock, turn the rock over. The current will drive any organisms into the sieve. Transfer the organisms to jars containing 70% ethyl alcohol. Examine the bottom of the rock with a hand lens for small sluggish or attached organisms. Add them to the jar of alcohol.

5. Record the number of each type of organism found on the bottom of a rock. Repeat this procedure with three or four rocks at each station.

Put all specimens from the same station in the same container. The specimens are to be taken to the classroom for identification.

6. Collect larger animals such as fish and snakes with a large net. While two students hold the net across the stream, the others should move quickly from upstream toward the net dislodging the rocks. Animals should be driven into the net. Place the collected organisms in large enamel trays for field identification. Determine the number of each kind of organism. After observation, select a few to take to the classroom for careful observation. Return the rest to the stream. Place the samples for lab identification in large jars or aquaria containing stream water. Refrigerate the containers upon returning to school.

7. Locate an area near each station in which the bottom contains mud or silt. Fill a medium jar one-third full of stream water. Fill the jar to the top with mud or silt from the sample area. Shake the material in the jar. Pour the material from the jar into a household sieve. Swirl the sieve in water to remove small soil particles. Place the contents on a white enamel tray. Examine the dead and decaying vegetation for the presence of animals and algae.

8. With forceps, place the organisms in containers for later analysis. Mark each container with the station number.

Part D: Classroom Analysis of Biota

1. Using taxonomic keys supplied by your teacher, identify the specimens found at each station. List and record the number of each organism found at each station.

2. For microscopic specimens, make wet mounts and observe the specimens with a compound microscope.

3. For macroscopic organisms, use a stereomicroscope or hand lens to observe the specimens if necessary.

Field Studies of a Freshwater Ecosystem

DATA AND ANALYSIS

1. In which area were insects more abundant, rapids or deeper pools? Why?

_____

_____

_____

2. Why should you expect fewer aquatic insects in the stream in late summer than in early spring?

_____

_____

_____

3. In which area were algae more abundant, rapids or deeper pools? Why?

_____

_____

_____

4. What physical factors are necessary for excessive algae growth?

_____

_____

5. Did the type of bottom at various stations have any bearing on the types of organisms found? Why?

_____

_____

_____

6. What special adaptations do plants and animals that live in either pools or rapids have?

_____

_____

_____

7. Is there any difference in the rate of flow at each station? Should there be any difference? Why?

_____

_____

_____

8. How does the color and turbidity of the water affect the presence or absence of certain organisms?

_____

_____

_____

9. Were there any differences in air and water temperatures throughout the study?

_____

_____

10. What physical factors could cause changes in the temperatures?

_____

_____

_____

11. Did the ppm of carbon dioxide change through-out the study? Explain.

_____

_____

_____

_____

12. Should you expect a change in carbon dioxide content or the pH throughout the study?

_____

_____

13. How can the pH and carbon dioxide content affect the life forms?

_____

_____

_____

14. Which phylum of animals is widely represented in the rapids? In the deeper pools? Explain.

_____

_____

_____

15. Which plant type is most widely represented, floating, emergent, or submerged? Why?

_____

_____

_____

Pre-AP Testing Water Quality

One way of judging water quality is to determine the amount of oxygen dissolved in the water. Oxygen may be supplied to a body of water from the air and from photosynthetic organisms living in the water. Clean water usually has a high oxygen content. Polluted water usually has a low oxygen content because organisms in the water use the oxygen as they decompose.

OBJECTIVES

In this investigation, you will

- measure the concentration of dissolved oxygen in water samples obtained from different locations using a dissolved oxygen probe.

- give reasons why the water samples have different concentrations of dissolved oxygen.

MATERIALS

LabPro or CBL 2 unit
AC adapter (optional)
TI graphing calculator
link cable
Vernier dissolved oxygen probe
sodium sulfite calibration solution
D.O. electrode filling solution

Beral pipette
dissolved oxygen calibration bottle
metric ruler
classroom thermometer
classroom barometer
water samples from different
 locations (4 or more)
jars with lids (4 or more)

plastic or rubber gloves
100-mL graduated cylinder
10-mL graduated cylinder
100-mL beakers (5)
distilled water
wax marking pencil
lab wipes

PROCEDURE

Part A: Set up the Dissolved Oxygen Probe

1. Connect the TI graphing calculator to the LabPro or CBL 2 interface using the link cable. Connect the dissolved oxygen probe into Channel 1 of the interface. If the dissolved oxygen probe needs to be warmed up, proceed to Step 2. If the probe has already been warmed up, proceed to Part B.

2. Unscrew the membrane cap (counterclockwise) from the tip of the electrode on the dissolved oxygen probe. Do not touch the membrane at the very tip of the probe.

3. Use a Beral pipet to fill the membrane cap with about 1 mL of D.O. electrode filling solution. Carefully thread the membrane cap (clockwise) onto the electrode body. Do not over tighten the cap. Rinse the electrode with distilled water and carefully wipe it dry with a lab wipe.

4. Place the dissolved oxygen probe in a 250-mL beaker containing about 75 mL of water.

5. Turn on the calculator and start the DATA-MATE program. Press CLEAR to reset the program.

   (a) If the calculator screen displays CH 1 DO (MG/L), proceed to Step 6. If it does not, continue with this step to manually select the dissolved oxygen probe.

   (b) Select SETUP from the main screen.

   (c) Press ENTER to select CH 1.

   (d) Select D. OXYGEN (MG/L) from the SELECT SENSOR menu.

   (e) Select OK to return to the main screen.

Lab
17

Testing Water Quality

PROCEDURE continued

6. Warm up the dissolved oxygen probe for 10 minutes.

(a) With the probe still in the water, wait 10 minutes while the probe warms up. The probe must stay connected to the interface at all times to keep it warmed up. If disconnected for a period longer than a few minutes, it will be necessary to warm it up again.

(b) At the end of class, leave the dissolved oxygen probe connected to the interface, with the DATAMATE program running. If this is done, the probe will stay warm and ready for the next class.

Figure 1

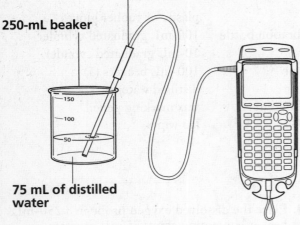

Dissolved oxygen probe

250-mL beaker

75 mL of distilled water

Part B: Calibrate the Dissolved Oxygen Probe

1. Select SETUP from the main screen.

2. Select CALIBRATE from the setup screen.

3. Select CALIBRATE NOW.

4. Determine the zero-oxygen calibration point.

(a) Remove the probe from the water and place the tip of the probe into the sodium sulfite calibration solution. **IMPORTANT:** *No air bubbles can be trapped below the tip of the probe or the probe will sense an inaccurate dissolved oxygen level.* If the voltage does not rapidly decrease, tap the side of the bottle with the probe to dislodge any bubbles. The readings should be in the 0.2- to 0.5-V range.

(b) When the voltage stabilizes (~1 minute), press ENTER .

(c) Enter "0" as the known concentration value in mg/L.

5. Determine the saturated DO calibration point.

(a) Rinse the probe with distilled water and gently blot dry.

(b) Unscrew the lid of the calibration bottle provided with the probe. Slide the lid and the grommet about 2 cm onto the probe body.

(c) Add water to the bottle to a depth of about 1 cm and screw the bottle into the cap, as shown. **IMPORTANT:** *Do not touch the membrane or get it wet during this step.*

(d) Keep the probe in this position for about a minute. The readings should be above 2.0 V. When the voltage stabilizes, press ENTER .

(e) Enter the correct saturated dissolved-oxygen value (in mg/L), from the Appendix on page 69, (for example, "8.66") using the current barometric pressure and air temperature values.

(f) Select OK to return to the setup screen.

(g) Select OK again to return to the main screen.

(h) Return the dissolved oxygen probe to the beaker of water.

Part C: Finding the Dissolved Oxygen Concentration of Various Water Samples

NOTE: *Proceed with this part of the lab only after the dissolved oxygen probe has been warmed up and calibrated.*

1. In jars, collect four or more water samples from different locations. Samples could come from a tap, a pond, a lake, a river, a puddle, or an aquarium. Try to find water that has been standing and has some algae growth. Fill the jars to the top, label by source, and seal with lids. **CAUTION:** *Wear protective gloves while collecting and handling water samples.* Record your observations of the water samples in Table 1. Indicate whether any look polluted or dirty.

Testing Water Quality

PROCEDURE continued

2. With the water samples at room temperature, gently pour 25 mL of each into separate 100-mL beakers labeled with each source. Pour slowly to avoid making bubbles.

3. Set up the calculator for data collection. Select SETUP from the main screen. Select MODE by pressing ⬆ once and then pressing ENTER. Select SINGLE POINT from the SELECT MODE menu. Select OK to return to the main screen.

4. Using a gentle motion, stir the dissolved oxygen probe through the water in one of the beakers. Make sure no bubbles are trapped under the tip of the probe. To provide an accurate reading, liquid must be continually moving past the membrane of the electrode. Once the reading displayed on the calculator screen has stabilized, select START to collect data. When data collection finishes, the dissolved oxygen concentration of the sample will be displayed on the screen.

Record the concentration in Table 1. Press ENTER to return to the main screen. Rinse the end of the probe with distilled water and place it in the next beaker to be tested.

5. Repeat Step 4 for the other water samples.

6. When finished, place the probe in a beaker of distilled water. Leave the DATAMATE program and calculator running for the next class. If you are the last class to use the equipment, exit the DATAMATE program and turn off the calculator. Disconnect the probe from the LabPro or CBL 2. Remove the membrane cap and rinse the inside and outside of the cap with distilled water. Rinse and carefully dry the exposed cathode and anode inner elements of the probe. Reinstall the membrane cap loosely onto the electrode body for storage.

7. At the conclusion of the lab, wash your hands thoroughly with soap and water.

DATA AND ANALYSIS

Table 1

Sample	Water Source	Observations of Water	Concentration of Dissolved Oxygen (ppm)
1			
2			
3			
4			

Testing Water Quality

Lab 17

| DATA AND ANALYSIS continued |

1. Explain why the water samples you collected have different concentrations of dissolved oxygen.

_____

_____

_____

2. A lake sample having less than 4 ppm of dissolved oxygen is harmful to aquatic life.

(a) Which of your samples could not support aquatic life?

_____

_____

(b) Explain why oxygen dissolved in water is important for aquatic life.

_____

_____

3. The graph in Figure 2 shows the values for dissolved oxygen in a lake at various depths. Explain what might cause the differences in the concentrations of dissolved oxygen.

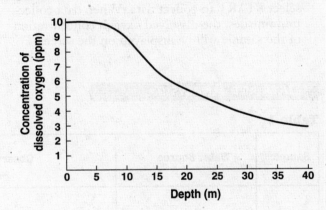

Figure 2

_____

_____

_____

_____

_____

4. List errors you may have made in Part C that could have affected your results.

_____

_____

_____

Appendix

Dissolved Oxygen Concentrations

Use this table to calibrate the dissolved oxygen probe used in Lab 17 *Testing Water Quality*.

Dissolved Oxygen (mg/L) in Air-Saturated Distilled Water								
	Barometric Pressure							
Air Temperature	770 mm Hg	760 mm Hg	750 mm Hg	740 mm Hg	730 mm Hg	720 mm Hg	710 mm Hg	700 mm Hg
17°C	9.86	9.74	9.61	9.48	9.35	9.22	9.10	8.97
18°C	9.67	9.54	9.41	9.29	9.16	9.04	8.91	8.79
19°C	9.47	9.35	9.23	9.11	8.98	8.86	8.74	8.61
20°C	9.29	9.17	9.05	8.93	8.81	8.69	8.57	8.45
21°C	9.11	9.00	8.88	8.76	8.64	8.52	8.40	8.28
22°C	8.94	8.83	8.71	8.59	8.48	8.36	8.25	8.13
23°C	8.78	8.66	8.55	8.44	8.32	8.21	8.09	7.98
24°C	8.62	8.51	8.40	8.28	8.17	8.06	7.95	7.84
25°C	8.47	8.36	8.25	8.14	8.03	7.92	7.81	7.70
26°C	8.32	8.21	8.10	7.99	7.89	7.78	7.67	7.56
27°C	8.17	8.07	7.96	7.86	7.75	7.64	7.54	7.43

LAB 1
Measuring Diffusion Rates
Objectives
Determine the effect of time and concentration on the diffusion of potassium permanganate into potato cubes.

Time Allotment
1 class period

Materials
beaker (100-mL)
wax pencil
potato
razor blade (single-edge)
small beakers (4)
clock or watch with second hand
5% potassium permanganate solution
1% potassium permanganate solution
0.1% potassium permanganate solution
forceps
metric ruler
water

Preparation
Prepare the potassium permanganate solutions before class. 500 mL of each solution should be adequate for one class of 24 students. Have students return solutions to separate large beakers at the end of the investigation for reuse in other classes. See page T8 for the preparation of the solutions.

Teaching the Lab
- Dialysis tubing may be used; however, plastic lunch bags are less expensive. Note: plastic bags are impermeable to glucose; dialysis tubing is not.
- Paper or plastic foam cups are recommended in place of glass beakers (potassium permanganate stains glassware).
- Certain brands of plastic bags may slow down passage of iodine into the bag. Thus, the procedure is to allow the experiment to remain set up for 24 hours before observing changes. Color changes are then much more obvious than if a shorter time is used.

Part A:
- In measuring diffusion, the distances are small. Students may have to measure in decimals of a millimeter.

- You may wish to have students start Part B as soon as Part A has been set up. A separate beaker of 5% potassium permanganate is not needed. Students may use the 5% solution from Part A.

Data and Analysis

Table 1. Potato Cubes in Solution for Different Lengths of Time		
Cube	Time in Solution (min)	Distance of Diffusion (mm)
1	0	0
2	10	0.5
3	20	0.8
4	30	1.5
5	40	2.0

Table 2. Potato Cubes in Solutions of Different Concentrations		
Cube	Concentration of Chemical	Distance of Diffusion (mm)
1	0.1%	0.2
2	1%	1.0
3	5%	2.0

Student paragraphs will vary, but students should refer to behavioral objectives ("In this investigation") as well as the introduction for information on the purpose of Parts A and B. Students should restate their findings giving actual data recorded. Use of data should enable students to cite trends observed in the investigation and to draw conclusions about the role of time and concentration of the chemical of diffusion.

LAB 2
Normal and Plasmolyzed Cells
Objectives
- Prepare a wet mount of an *Elodea* leaf in tap water and a wet mount of an *Elodea* leaf in salt water for microscopic observation.
- Observe and diagram cells of both wet mounts.
- Observe the normal appearance of *Elodea* cells in tap water.
- Compare normal cells in tap water to plasmolyzed cells in salt water.

Time Allotment
1 class period

Materials
microscope
microscope slide

coverslips
Elodea (water plant)
dropper
water
6% salt solution
forceps

Preparation

Prepare the 6% salt solution as described on page T8. Put a few milliliters into each of 24 small beakers, test tubes, or dropper bottles.

Teaching the Lab

- Remind students to be sure that the two liquids on the slide do not run together.
- Allow a few minutes for plasmolysis to occur.
- In salt water, the contents of the cell "shrink" to the center of the cell. The cell membrane pulls away from the cell wall (as water is lost from the cell) and encloses the cell contents near the cell center.

Data and Analysis

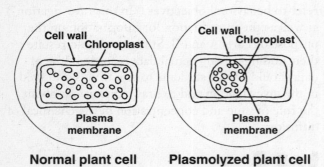

Normal plant cell   **Plasmolyzed plant cell**

1. evenly distributed
2. bunched together
3. (a) 99%
   (b) 99%
   (c) They are the same.
   (d) No; the same amount of water entered and left the cell at all times.
4. (a) 94%
   (b) 99%
   (c) higher inside
   (d) when water concentrations differ
   (e) high to low
   (f) yes; water moved from high concentration to low, and the cell shrunk in size.

5. "shrinking" of cell contents due to loss of water from a cell

LAB 3
Extracellular Enzymes
Objectives

Distinguish the degree of extracellular digestion that occurs as a result of bacterial growth on agar plates containing starch or milk.

Time Allotment

2 class periods (separated by 2–4 days)

Materials

broth cultures:
  Bacillus cereus
  Bascillus subtilis
  Escherichia coli
  yeast suspension
wax pencil
incubator
iodine solution (15 mL)
5% skim milk agar (15 mL)
0.2% starch agar (15 mL)
0.4% starch agar (15 mL)
0.8% starch agar (15 mL)
sterile cotton swabs (8)
sterile petri dishes (4)

Preparation

- Ten cultures of each broth culture are needed for each class of 30.
- Prepare plates prior to class to save time. Place each type of plate several stations apart so students do not mix them up.

Teaching the Lab

- Have students label the plates immediately.
- Make sure students add enough iodine to completely cover the agar.

Data and Analysis

Hydrolysis of Starch			
	0.8% Starch	0.4% Starch	0.2% Starch
B. cereus	+	+	++
B. subtilis	+	+	++
E coli	+	+	Very slight
Yeast	-	-	-

++ = more complete digestion
+ = less complete digestion
- = no digestion

Hydrolysis of Milk Proteins

Culture Type	Observations
B. cereus	Less complete digestion
B. subtilis	No digestion
E coli	Less complete digestion
Yeast	No digestion

1. To prevent water from dropping on the agar surface and spreading colonies of bacteria and yeast all over the plate.

2. *B. subtilis* and *B. cereus* digest starch better than *E coli.*

3. Yes, the plate with the greatest concentration of starch (0.8%) should show little digestion while the least concentration (0.2%) should show more digestion.

4. yeast

5. The enzyme for starch digestion is absent in yeast. It is present in the three bacteria species.

6. 0.2% starch. The starch is less concentrated on this plate.

7. *B. cereus* and *B. subtilis*. They have the enzymes present to digest the milk proteins.

8. *B. subtilis* and *B. cereus* because they contain enzymes for both starch and protein digestion.

LAB 4

How does the environment affect mitosis?

Objectives
- Prepare squashes of onion root tips to observe mitosis.
- Make a hypothesis to describe the effect of caffeine on mitosis.
- Compare growth of onion roots in water and in caffeine.

Time Allotment
2–3 class periods

Materials
compound light microscopes (30)
microscope slides (30)
paper towels (1 roll)
coverslips (30)
forceps (30)
Elodea (several sprigs)
droppers (60)

tap water
6% salt solution (200 mL)

Preparation
- Buy onion bulbs from a garden center. To save time, do steps 2 and 3 of Part A for students. It should take about 2 days for the roots to reach 1 cm. To save more time, do steps 1 and 3 of Part B the day before the lab. Leaving the tips in the fixative for 24 hours eliminates the need for the water bath in step 4.
- See page T8 to prepare the solution.

Teaching the Lab
Have students work in groups of four.

Data and Analysis
Data for Table 1 will vary, but students will probably find that roots grown in pure water will reach 1 cm in 2–3 days. The table is equivalent to day 3 in Table 2 of the lab.

% Caffeine	# of Roots	Average Length (mm)
0.0 (pure water)	41	21
0.1	35	11
0.3	26	9
0.5	25	6
0.6	25	6

Table 3 should show that there is a graded decrease in the number of cells in metaphase, anaphase, and telophase from the lowest to the highest percent of caffeine. In water-treated roots, about 80% of cells are found in interphase.

1. Answers will vary. Most should hypothesize that increasing the concentration of caffeine would alter the frequency of mitotic stages in the root tips.

2. The control is the bulb treated in plain water; the variable is the concentration of caffeine.

3. Answers will vary. In general, students will find that the rate of growth decreases with higher concentrations of caffeine.

4. In cells from the water treatment, students probably will observe all phases of mitosis. The caffeine-treated roots probably will show the highest percentage of metaphase cells. With increased concentrations of caffeine, there will be fewer cells completing cell division and probably no cells in anaphase or telophase.

5. Answers will vary, but students probably will find a direct correlation. The higher the concentration of caffeine, the slower the rate of root growth and the fewer cells found in metaphase, anaphase, and telophase.

6. Answers may include ultraviolet light, pH, temperature, and various pollutants.

7. Students who hypothesized as in answer 1 will say their hypotheses were supported.

LAB 5
Observation of Meiosis
Objectives
- Observe the stages of meiosis in lily anthers.
- Draw and label the stages of meiosis in lily anthers.

Time Allotment
1 class period

Materials
compound light microscope
prepared slide of lily anther
drawing paper (optional)
pencil (colored pencils if desired)

Preparation
- Prepared slides of lily anthers can be purchased from biological supply houses.
- Check all microscopes to ensure that lamps are not burned out and that lenses focus properly.

Teaching the Lab
- Students should work individually if there are enough microscopes.
- Go over the phases of meiosis with the class, using Figure 1 as a guide.
- Encourage students to move the slides around on the microscope stage in order to observe various stages of meiosis.

Data and Analysis
Student drawings should resemble those in Figure 1. All drawings should be labeled with the appropriate stage of meiosis.

1. Answers will vary. Meiosis occurs in great frequency in anthers. Members of the lily family have few and very large chromosomes.

2. Answers will vary. Metaphase I, metaphase II, and anaphase II usually are abundant.

3. chromosomes should appear as colored, threadlike objects within the cells.

4. Meiosis produces gametes containing half the number of chromosomes found in body cells. It allows plants to produce offspring with the same number of chromosomes found in the parent plants.

LAB 6
Influencing the Rate of Photosynthesis
Objectives
- Assemble the equipment needed to measure the rate of photosynthesis in *Elodea*.
- Count bubbles of oxygen gas given off by *Elodea* to determine the rate of photosynthesis.

Time Allotment
1 class period

Materials
Elodea (water plant)
test tube (large size)
water, warm (room-temperature)
sodium bicarbonate powder
lamp (40-watt)
tape
razor blade (single-edge)
metric ruler
metal stand
glass rod (17-cm-long)

Preparation
Keep *Elodea* in bright light overnight before the investigation is performed.

Teaching the Lab
- Anacharis may be used in place of *Elodea*.
- If spring water or dechlorinated water is available, use it in place of tap water.
- If a higher wattage bulb is used, water temperature will rise, introducing a new variable into the investigation.
- Students may have to remove as much as 4–5 cm of plant.
- 2–3 cm of stem should be cut off. Trim stem to a gradual point with the razor blade.
- The glass rod prevents the plant from twisting inside of the test tube. A straw or coffee stirrer can also be used.

- Lamp must be directly opposite plant to achieve good results.
- Trials may be extended to 10 minutes if time permits.
- The exact amount of sodium bicarbonate is not critical.
- Results of this experiment are sometimes marginal. Some plants will provide bubbles of oxygen if properly cut and crushed; others will not. If time permits, pre-test and use only those plants which do provide oxygen bubbles.

Data and Analysis

Environment Condition	Number of Oxygen Bubbles		
	Trial 1	Trial 2	Trial 3
Lamp 5 cm from plant	50	62	56
Lamp 20 cm from plant	27	24	25.5
Plant in sodium bicarbonate; lamp 5 cm from plant	78	84	81

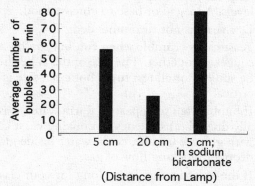

(Distance from Lamp)

1. The number of oxygen bubbles produced in a specific period of time.
2. (a) Photosynthesis slows down.
   (b) *Elodea* is receiving less light energy.
   (c) When more light energy is received, photosynthesis occurs at a faster rate.
3. (a) The rate of photosynthesis increased.
   (b) Carbon dioxide is needed for photosynthesis. Thus, supplying more CO_2 increases the rate.
4. Student graphs will vary.
   (a) Increasing the light will increase the rate of photosynthesis.
   (b) Photosynthesis requires light energy. Without it, no photosynthesis will occur.
   (c) Reducing light will reduce rate of photosynthesis.

LAB 7
Chloroplast Pigment Analysis
Objectives
- Remove pigments from spinach by boiling it in water and then heating it in ethyl alcohol.
- Separate the pigments from one another by using a technique called chromatography.
- Identify the pigments by their colors and positions on the chromatogram.
- Determine relative amounts of each pigment.

Time Allotment
1 class period

Materials
test-tube holder
filter paper (strip type)
cork
thumbtack
spinach (frozen package that has been defrosted)
solvent
glass rod
water
metric ruler
glass pipette
forceps
scissors
hot plate
beaker (600-mL)
ethyl alcohol
beaker (400-mL)
small container
oven mitts (2)

Preparation
You may wish to prepare the pigment solution (Part A). From this preparation, enough pigment will be made available for the entire class.

Teaching the Lab
- Any green leaf may be used as a pigment source (geranium, grass, bean). Carrot leaves are most suitable. They provide a good source of carotene.
- Use denatured ethyl alcohol. Acetone may be used to extract chlorophyll from the leaf.
- Extract must be very dark green with a minimum of alcohol used to remove pigments.
- Wrapping the spinach in cheesecloth and then

squeezing tightly to wring out all water is a helpful technique.

Data and Analysis

1. The filter paper strip had several bands, each a different color.
2. (a) several
   (b) Several bands were present on the filter paper strip.
3. Substances can be separated from one another and identified.
4. (a) Answers will vary.
   (b) Answers will vary.
5. (a) xanthophyll I and xanthophyll II
   (b) chlorophyll a and chlorophyll b
6. (a) chloroplasts
   (b) chlorophyll a absorbs light energy in the process of photosynthesis.
   (c) These pigments absorb wavelengths of light energy different from chlorophyll a.
7. A dark green leaf probably contains more chlorophyll b.
8. Once chlorophyll a and b are destroyed, other pigments in lesser quantities may be seen.

LAB 8
Factors Influencing the Rate of Yeast Respiration

Objectives

- Count and record bubbles of carbon dioxide gas given off by respiring yeast cells.
- Compare respiration rates at two different temperatures.
- Compare respiration rates when using different foods for the yeast cells.

Time Allotment

1 class period

Materials

yeast cake
droppers
test tubes
one-hole stoppers to fit test tubes
20% glucose solution
cold water
clay (optional)
ice
straight pins
tape
warm water
thermometer
wax pencil
quart milk cartons with tops cut off
yeast food A
yeast food B
yeast food C
yeast food D
cloth towel
graduated cylinder

Preparation

See page T9 for preparation of solution.

Teaching the Lab

- You may wish to extend this investigation by having students design and perform an experiment which determines differences in respiration rate when using foods with different pH levels. Add acid or base to glucose food.
- Dry yeast is not recommended.
- Yeast cakes crumble when cut, but can be squeezed together. The size of the cube should be similar for all test tubes but exact size is not critical.
- If bubbles fail to appear in warm water, it is usually due to: (a) student's not mixing yeast cube with glucose in tube, or (b) water inside glass dropper blocking flow of gas.
- If the investigation is too long for your class period, reduce each trial to seven or eight minutes.
- Caution students about water getting into the dropper from inside the tube. The glass portion of the medicine dropper must be free of any liquid.

Data and Analysis

Yeast Respiration Rates Number of Bubbles per Min						
Time (min)	38°C	10°C	Food A Fructose	Food B Water	Food C Lactose	Food D Sucrose
1	0	0	0	0	0	2
2	3	0	7	0	1	12
3	8	0	6	0	3	15
4	11	0	10	0	5	18
5	12	1	15	0	4	17
6	15	1	14	0	6	20
7	18	0	13	0	8	15
8	22	2	17	0	7	23
9	25	0	18	0	10	25
10	31	0	14	0	5	22

Total Bubbles in 10 Min		
	Your Data	Class Average
Cold Water	0	3
Warm Water	145	162
Food A	114	110
Food B	0	0
Food C	49	60
Food D	169	183

Student paragraphs for 1 and 2 will vary but should include:

(a) using performance objectives on page 23 ("In this investigation" section)

(b) see answer (a)

(c) stating that the organism used is yeast

(d) stating that respiration is a series of chemical reactions that speed up as temperature increases

(e) using data from cold and warm trials to show that respiration rate is influenced by temperature

(f) support from student and class average data for a more rapid respiration rate at warmer temperatures

(g) reasons for lack of total agreement between student data and class averages: errors in counting, different starting temperatures, warm water cooling at different rates during the experiment, cold water warming at different rates during experiment, different amounts of yeast cube used, and so on.

Question 3 requires students to see the connection between rate of respiration and ATP production. More respiration (more CO_2 released) indicates more ATP production.

Question 4 requires students to record respiration rates of known sugars of the three types. Proper controls should be used; sugar concentrations for all three types should be equal.

LAB 9
How can genetically engineered plants be multiplied?
Objectives
Use micropropagation to produce new shoots form tiny pieces of African violet leaves.

Time Allotment
1 class period the first day; 5 minutes once a week for 5 weeks

Materials
African violet medium
liquid dish detergent
distilled water
bleach
glass jars with lids
sugar
agar
aluminum foil
NaOH
HCl

Preparation
- You can obtain African violet medium from a biological supply company.
- Prepare the culture medium in advance.
- See page T10 for preparation of solutions.
- Sterile water for the rinses can be prepared by placing loosely capped bottles or other glass containers of distilled water in a boiling water bath for 10 min. After cooling, keep the sterile water capped until ready for use.
- Sterilize razor blades and forceps by wrapping them in aluminum foil and baking them in a conventional oven at 350°F for 15 min.

Teaching the Lab
- Divide the class into pairs to work on the lab. Have one partner prepare the culture medium (Part B) while the other partner disinfects the leaves (Part C).
- Provide students with an undisturbed place to keep their cultures under fluorescent lights and

out of direct sunlight for 16 h/day a day at about 25°C.

- If a sterile environment was not maintained, contamination will be apparent within a few days. Make sure any contaminated Petri dishes are discarded promptly.
- Shoots should start growing in about two weeks and be visible with the unaided eye in five weeks.

Data and Analysis

1. It is crucial to maintain aseptic conditions to avoid contamination of the culture medium. If aseptic conditions are not maintained, bacteria or fungi are likely to contaminate and take over the medium and infect the plant tissues.

2. Plant micropropagation allows genetic engineers to propagate large numbers of genetically identical plants from tiny pieces of genetically altered tissues. Other propagation techniques are slower and require much larger pieces of plant material.

3. It is possible because each cell of a plant holds all the DNA of the organism and thus, can lead to the development of an entire plant.

4. Using micropropagation, breeders and growers can propagate plants asexually to produce millions of new plants from a single plant. This allows them to introduce new cultivars far sooner than if they were using conventional propagation techniques.

LAB 10
Making Test Crosses
Objectives
- Learn to care for and raise two generations of fruit flies.
- Perform two test crosses with fruit flies.
- Observe the phenotypic results of the two test crosses.
- Infer the genotypes of the parental fruit flies and their offspring.
- Construct Punnett squares for two test crosses.

Time Allotment
3 class periods, each about two weeks apart; daily inspection of vials

Materials
instant *Drosophila* medium (1 bag)

culture vials with foam plugs (16)
cultures of vestigial-winged fruit flies (8)
cultures of normal-winged fruit flies (8)
vials of alcohol (8)
anesthetic (8 vials)
anesthetic wands (8)
white index cards (8)
fine-tipped paintbrushes (8)
wax pencils (8)
stereomicroscopes or hand lenses (8)
laboratory aprons (30)
goggles (30)

Preparation
- *Drosophila* cultures and medium should be ordered at least three weeks in advance.
- Prepare the vials of medium for students to use for their test crosses.
- Fruit flies, vials, foam plugs, and instant medium can be obtained from most biological supply houses. An anesthetic other than ether can be obtained from a biological supply vendor.

Teaching the Lab
Have students work in groups of four.

- Virgin female flies can be obtained for about six hours after new flies emerge. All adults must be removed from the vials prior to emergence.
- Review the life cycle of *Drosophila* with students. Show what the larval and pupal stages look alike.
- Demonstrate how to anesthetize and collect flies, cautioning students not to overanesthetize or crush the flies.
- Pooling of data probably will produce results that more closely approximate expected results.
- A fruit fly cycle takes two weeks at 20°C. This lab will take three periods—one to set up the initial test cross, another session two weeks later to set up the second test cross, and a third to sort and count the offspring of the second test cross and complete the questions. Students will have to check the vials regularly to determine the right times to start the test crosses.
- Have virgin female vestigial flies available for Part B.

Data and Analysis

In test cross 1, students should observe that all TC_1 flies are normal-winged. In test cross 2, about half of the TC_2 flies should be normal-winged and half should be vestigial-winged.

1. Because vestigial wings are recessive, the females exhibiting this feature must be homozygous 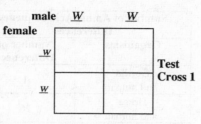 for this trait (ww). Because all of the offspring were normal long-winged, the male normal-winged parental flies must be homozygous for this trait (WW).

2. All flies in the TC_1 generation had normal wings.

3. The genotype of the flies of the TC_1 generation was Ww. Each of the offspring received a dominant allele from the male parent and a recessive allele from the female parent.

4. See Punnett square 1.

5. The females were ww and the males were Ww.

6. About half the flies should have normal wings, while the other half should have vestigial wings.

7. The normal long-winged flies are Ww. The vestigial-winged flies are ww. These flies each received a recessive allele from the female parent, and either a recessive or a dominant allele from the male parent.

8. See Punnett square 2.

9. The expected ratio would be 1:1. The observed ratio may vary slightly.

LAB 11
How is camouflage an adaptive advantage?

Objectives

- Use an artificial environment to model the concept of natural selection.
- Hypothesize what will happen if natural selection acts over time on organisms exhibiting camouflage.
- Construct bar graphs to show the results of the lab.
- Compare the model of natural selection in the lab to real examples of natural selection.

Time Allotment

1 class period

Materials

hole punches (8)
colored paper (8 sheets each of purple, brown, blue, green, tan, black, orange, red, yellow, and white)
plastic film canisters or petri dishes (80)
pieces of brightly colored, floral fabric (80-cm × 80-cm) (8)
graph paper (60 sheets)
goggles (30)

Preparation

Assemble all materials before beginning this lab.

Teaching the Lab

Students should work in groups of four.

- To save time, you can punch out all the dots prior to class. Have a hole punch and sheets of colored paper available though, because students may need additional dots of some colors.
- Each team will have different results, depending on the colors present on the cloth. You can purchase the same color and pattern cloth for each group or have different colors and patterns for different groups. If all groups have the same kind of cloth, the groups can pool their results. Graphs can then be made of the class data.
- The various colors on the cloths could be used to demonstrate the fact that Earth has various biomes with different colored features.
- The dots can be saved from year to year in the petri dishes or film canisters.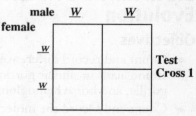

Data and Analysis

Data will vary, depending on the colors and patterns on the cloths.

1. Hypothesis: Dots of the predominant colors on the cloth will become more numerous with each succeeding generation. Dots that contrast with the colors on the cloth will become less numerous with each succeeding generation.

2. Answers will vary. The colors that stand out against the background of the cloth most likely will be picked up.

3. Answers will vary. The colors that blend into the background of the cloth will least likely be picked up because they will not be seen as easily.

4. The predator will not see the food.

5. Answers will vary. Some examples are polar bears, chameleons, and walkingstick insects.

6. Those colors that blend in with the background increase in number, while colors that stand out decrease in number.

7. There would be little or no change in the frequency of the colors over time, since no one color would be more likely to be picked up than another.

8. If the dots were bad-tasting, stung, or possessed other characteristics that the predator found undesirable, it would learn to associate the color with these characteristics and would avoid eating those dots.

9. Accept all reasonable answers. Examples are living stones, yellow crab spider, some caterpillars, any mottled-colored moth, and many snakes and birds.

10. Answers will vary. Students who predicted that dots of predominant fabric colors would become more numerous and that dots of colors that contrast with the fabric would become less numerous will say that their hypotheses were supported.

LAB 12

Biochemical Evidence for Evolution

Objectives

- Count and record differences in the sequence of amino acids in similar portions of human, gorilla, and horse hemoglobin.
- Count and record the molecules of each amino acid present in similar portions of human, gorilla, and horse hemoglobin.
- Use these data to show how biochemical evidence can be used to support evolution.

Time Allotment

1 class period

Teaching the Lab

- This lab is designed for independent study. It shows how biochemical evidence contributes ot

the understanding of evolutionary processes. It also requires students to refer to the role of DNA in protein formation.

- There are 146 amino acids for each organism.

Data and Analysis

Number of Amino Acid Sequence Differences	
Organisms	Number of Differences
Gorilla and human	1
Horse and human	26
Gorilla and horse	26

1. in red blood cells

2. protein, composed of amino acids, chemical molecule

3. 17

4. (a) leucine
   (b) valine
   (c) methionine

5. (a) very similar
   (b) not too similar
   (c) not too similar

Number of Each Amino Acid				
Amino Acid	Abbreviation	Human	Gorilla	Horse
Alanine	Ala	15	15	15
Arginine	Arg	3	2	4
Aspartic acid	Asp	13	13	14
Cysteine	Cys	2	2	1
Glutamic acid	Glu	11	11	14
Glycine	Gly	13	13	14
Histidine	His	9	9	9
Leucine	Leu	18	19	19
Lysine	Lys	11	11	11
Methionine	Met	1	1	1
Phenylalanine	Phe	8	8	8
Proline	Pro	7	7	5
Serine	Ser	5	5	6
Threonine	Thr	7	7	3
Tryptophan	Try	2	2	2
Tyrosine	Tyr	3	3	3
Valine	Val	18	18	17

6. (a) 16
   (b) 7
   (c) 8

7. (a) very similar
   (b) not too similar
   (c) not too similar
8. human and gorilla
9. human and gorilla
10. three bases differ
11. a mutation
12. If the sequence of amino acids is nearly alike, then the DNA base sequences are almost identical. The statement is supported.
13. Close biochemical similarity indicates chromosome similarity. The statement is supported.

LAB 13
Transpiration in Plants

Objectives
- Assemble a photometer
- Determine the rate of transpiration in a given plant species.
- Determine the effect of certain environmental factors on transpiration rate.

Time Allotment
1 class period

Materials
burner
iron stand
test-tube clamp
glass tubing (20 cm)
rubber tubing (two 6-cm sections)
beaker (1000-mL)
paper toweling
water
beaker large enough to hold the "U" tube
pipettes (5-mL) (2)
cord (10 cm)
razor blade or scalpel
potted plant
electric fan
spotlight or other bright light
petroleum jelly

Preparation
Assemble the photometer prior to lab to save time.

Teaching the Lab
- Potted plants such as *Coleus*, *Gernaium*, and *Zebrina* work best.
- Place sawdust or vermiculite in the bottom of the beaker (about 3 cm) to prevent breakage of the "U" tube.
- A disposable, plastic syringe without a needle is handy for filling the pipette. These syringes can be obtained from a local hospital or nursing home.
- The plant can be supported in the photometer by use of a second clamp.
- Allow 5–10 min for the plant to return to normal before using the light. A 100- or 150-W bulb may be used in place of a spotlight.
- A cotton swab can be used to apply petroleum jelly.
- Leaf surface area can be important. To be quantitative, the students would have to measure the surface areas of the leaf. Suggest other distances for the fan and light.

Data and Analysis

Individual Data on Amount of Water Transpired			
Condition	Plant Used	mL of Water Transpired	mL of Water Transpired Per Hour
Normal	*Coleus*	0.0	0.0
Fan	*Coleus*	1.0	6.0
Spotlight	*Coleus*	0.5	3.0
Petroleum jelly (upper surface)	*Coleus*	0.9	4.5
Petroleum jelly (both surfaces)	*Coleus*	0.0	0.0

Class Data on Amount of Water Transpired					
	mL of Water Transpired Per Hour				
Type of Plant	Normal	Fan	Spotlight	Petroleum Jelly (Upper Surface)	Petroleum Jelly (Both Surfaces)
Coleus	0.0	6.0	3.0	4.5	0.0
Geranium	0.0	7.5	3.6	4.0	0.0

1. light and wind
2. increase in temperature, decrease in relative humidity
3. Covering the stomata with petroleum jelly simulates the closing of stomata.

4. The larger the leaf surface, the greater the transpiration rate, provided there are numerous stomata.

5. cuticle and upper epidermis because water can transpire through them

6. The fan and spotlight simulate wind and light. These increase transpiration rate. The petroleum jelly closes the stomata and covers the cuticle, thus reducing the transpiration rate.

7. The fan causes water to leave the leaf at a faster rate through the stomata.

8. *Geranium, Coleus, Zebrina*

9. The number of stomata per cubic millimeter and the thickness of the cuticle vary.

10. Yes, allowing the plant to transpire normally before using the fan or bright light was a control.

11. relative humidity of the room, intensity of the light, and temperature of the room.

12. These factors introduced variables into the experiment. More or less water may have transpired if these factors were controlled.

LAB 14
The Human Heart
Objectives
- Follow the pathway of blood through the heart.
- Determine the amount of oxygen or carbon dioxide contained in blood in each side of the heart.
- Follow the sequence of events occurring as a heart beats.
- Measure blood pressure differences in arteries and veins using a heart-blood vessel model.

Time Allotment
1 class period

Materials
plastic bottle
2-hole stopper to fit bottle
metric ruler
glass tube, 3 cm long
glass tube, 18 cm long
plastic tube, 15 cm long

Preparation
You may wish to pre-assemble the blood pressure model (stopper and tubes).

Teaching the Lab
- The major concept for Part A is to make sure students understand the role of the right and left heart sides.
- The major concept for Part B is to make sure students understand that all blood received by or pumped from the right side is deoxygenated while the left side receives and pumps only oxygenated blood.
- While ventricles are in systole, atria are in diastole. While ventricles are in diastole, atria are in systole.
- The heartbeat is actually sound caused by closing of the valves.
- In Part D, to prevent water flowing from both tubes from joining into one stream, stick a small wads of paper between the glass and plastic tubes.
- It may be necessary to add more water to the bottles for repeating the trials.

Data and Analysis
Part A
1. lungs
2. lungs
Part B
3. (a) deoxygenated
   (b) oxygenated
Part C
4. (a) filling
   (b) being emptied
Part D
5. (a) plastic
   (b) glass
6. (a) glass
   (b) plastic
7. (a) glass
   (b) plastic
8. (a) glass
   (b) plastic

Blood Flow		
Receives Blood from		
Left side	1.	Left lung
	2.	Right lung
Right side	1.	Head
	2.	Body and legs
Pumps Blood to		
Left side	1.	Head
	2.	Body and legs
Right side	1.	Left lung
	2.	Right lung

Oxygen Content of Blood	
Chamber or Vessel	**Oxygenated or Deoxygenated**
Left ventricle	Oxygenated
Right ventricle	Deoxygenated
Left atrium	Oxygenated
Right atrium	Deoxygenated
Pulmonary artery	Deoxygenated
Pulmonary vein	Oxygenated
Superior vena cava	Deoxygenated
Inferior vena cava	Deoxygenated
Aorta	Oxygenated

	Ventricles In	
	Diastole	**Systole**
Relaxed or pumping	Relaxed	Pumping
Bi- and tricuspid valves open or closed?*	Open	Closed
Blood flowing past bi- and tricuspid valves?	Yes	No
Blood flowing into ventricles from atria?	Yes	No
Semilunar valves open or closed?*	Closed	Open
Blood flowing past semilunar valves?	No	Yes
Blood flowing out of ventricles into aorta or pulmonary artery?	No	yes
*Valves are open if ther tips are not touching.		

Student answers may vary. However, stream from glass tube should exceed stream from plastic tube.

Experimental Results		
	Glass Tube	**Plastic Tube**
Trial 1	142 mm	128 mm
Trial 2	140 mm	132 mm
Trial 3	146 mm	140 mm
Trial 4	138 mm	130 mm
Trial 5	140 mm	135 mm
Average Distance	141.2 mm	133 mm

1. (a) blood high in oxygen and low in carbon dioxide

(b) blood low in oxygen and high in carbon dioxide

(c) pumping (contracted) condition of ventricles

(d) relaxed condition of ventricles

2. deoxygenated to oxygenated

3. (a) to all parts of the body

(b) to the lungs

(c) to the right and left ventricles

4. (a) from head

(b) from body

(c) from lungs

5. Blood enters right atrium from superior and inferior vena cava while atrium is in diastole. Right atrium undergoes systole and blood is pumped past tricuspid valve into right ventricle, which is now in diastole. Right ventricle undergoes systole and blood is pumped past semilunar valve into pulmonary artery.

6. Blood enters left atrium from pulmonary veins while atrium is in diastole. Left atrium undergoes systole and blood is pumped past bicuspid valve into left ventricle, which is now in diastole. Left ventricle undergoes systole and blood is pumped past semilunar valve into aorta.

7. (a) Answers will vary.

(b) Answers will vary.

8. (a) Blood movement through the heart would stop.

(b) Blood movement through the heart would stop.

9. (a) heart

(b) blood

(c) veins

(d) arteries

10. (a) B; B is thicker, is more rigid, has more muscle tissue

(b) A; A is thin, is less rigid, has less muscle tissue

LAB 15
Earthworm Behavior
Objectives

- Conduct experiments that will show earthworms' unlearned responses to light and to gravity.

- Observe and record earthworm behavior.
- Contribute your data to class totals.
- Use class data to determine which experiment provides more easily interpretable earthworm behavior.

Time Allotment

1 class period

Materials

live earthworms
shoe box (or shoe box lid)
paper towels
black paper
scissors
tape
lamp
cardboard
metric ruler
clock or watch with second hand
water

Preparation

Have students collect worms from the ground or purchase them from a biological supply house or bait store.

Teaching the Lab

- Students should work in groups of four.
- Each team should have more than one worm.
- If lamps are in short supply, have half of the class perform Part B first. If no lamps are available, conduct Part A in a bright light outdoors or next to a classroom window.
- If time is short, reduce the number of trials or have half of the class do Part A, the other half Part B.

Data and Analysis

Student data will vary. However, the trend is that the anterior end is light sensitive (animal is negatively phototactic). Data for this part of the lab will show sharp differences between response of anterior and posterior ends to light.

	Response to Light			
	Anterior End in Light at Start		Anterior End in Dark at Start	
Trial	Anterior end in Light	Dark	Anterior end in Light	Dark
1	0	3	0	3
2	0	3	0	3
3	0	3	1	2
4	1	2	0	3
5	0	3	0	3
Individual totals	1	14	1	14
Class totals	4	146	7	143

Student data will vary. However, no specific trend may be observed. Measuring worm responses to gravity may not yield meaningful data.

1. The behavior tested was an earthworm's response to light.
2. (a) Anterior ends turn about and move into or toward a dark area.

    (b) Posterior ends do not move away from light (as long as anterior ends are in the dark).
3. All areas do not respond equally. Posterior ends do not respond to light; anterior ends respond by moving away from light.
4. (a) yes

    (b) This response could keep them under ground during the day and may help them avoid dessication.

	Response to Gravity								
	Worms Flat on Desk			Worms Facing Up Away from Gravity			Worms Facing Down Toward Gravity		
Trial	Anterior End Over Line	Anterior End Behind Line	No Change	Anterior End Over Line	Anterior End Behind Line	No Change	Anterior End Over Line	Anterior End Behind Line	No Change
1	1	2	0	1	2	0	0	3	0
2	2	0	1	0	3	0	0	2	1
3	3	0	0	2	1	0	3	0	0
4	0	1	2	0	1	2	1	2	0
5	0	2	1	0	3	0	2	1	0
6	1	1	1	1	2	0	2	1	0
7	2	0	1	1	1	1	0	2	1
8	0	2	1	1	2	0	1	2	0
9	0	3	0	0	1	2	1	1	1
10	2	1	0	1	2	0	0	1	2
Individual totals	11	12	7	7	18	5	10	15	5
Class totals	107	128	65	100	118	82	93	131	76

5. The behavior being tested is an earthworm's response to gravity.

6. Results are not conclusive.

7. (a) Part A

(b) Part A gives consistent results; Part B does not.

8. Many trials may be needed. Small differences in data may be difficult to determine.

LAB 16
Field Studies of a Freshwater Ecosystem

Objectives
- Set-up seven stations on a freshwater stream.
- Observe, distinguish, and record various physical factors of the stream.
- Observe, describe, and identify the organisms of the stream.
- Compare and analyze the relationship of the physical factors to the organisms form the collected data.

Time Allotment
This lab will take about 3 hours in the field. Then 4–5 more hours will be needed in the lab for further analysis.

Materials
Field Materials:

hammer
stakes or large nails (14)
cord (100 m)
metersticks (3)
white lid from jar
graph paper (8 sheets)
capped plastic bottle
baby food jars (3 to 4 dozen)
small jars (4)
medium jars (4)
large jars (4)
Celsius thermometers (2)
sample bottles (100-mL) (1 to 2 dozen)
phenolphthalein (25 mL)
pipette with 0.1-mL graduations
0.4% sodium hydroxide (50 mL)
pH kit
large plastic bags (1 dozen)
household sieve, large
70% ethyl alcohol (4–6 liters)
net, 1.5-m × 3 m
white enamel trays, large (2)
forceps
glass marker
watch with second hand

Classroom Analysis
microscopes (3)
stereomicroscopes (3)
coverslips (3)

Copyright © Glencoe/McGraw-Hill, a division of The McGraw-Hill Companies, Inc.

glass slides (3)
hand lens
dropper

Preparation

- Disposable baby formula bottles may be used for the 100-mL sample bottles.
- Purchase nylon net because it does not have to be dried.

Teaching the Lab

- This lab also can be done by one to seven students as an independent or group project. Results can be presented to the class.
- If time permits, a comparison of two streams would prove interesting. Once could be a fast-moving mountain stream, the other a slow-moving stream that flows through a meadow. Similar species will be found in each stream. Many different species also will be noted.
- While setting up stations, emphasize that disturbing the bottom will interfere with some of the physical and chemical tests.

Part A

- When examining the color and turbidity of the water, you may want to set up comparison jars that are clear, light, and dark. This can be achieved by adding no silt to one jar of water, a small amount of silt to a second jar, and a larger amount to a third jar.

Part B

- Caution students not to pour chemicals into the stream. Dispose of chemicals properly.

Part C

- Mosses can be found in water as "accidental" plants. Mosses grow on rocks because of moisture. When the stream increases in depth because of rainfall, it appears the mosses grow underwater.
- Some algae will not be attached to rocks. Some will be found in slower-moving water as floating masses. Some will be "caught" on logs and other vegetation. To keep algae for lab identification, put only a small amount (the size of a pea seed) in 100 mL of stream of water. Place in a lighted area in the lab.
- While collecting bottom-dwelling animals, several other students may stand behind these people with sieves to catch the smaller organisms that go through the nets.
- Aquatic insects and small vertebrates can be returned alive. Organisms living in fast-moving

water have higher oxygen demands than can be supplied in a small jar. To keep the organisms overnight, add an air stone attached to an aquarium pump. For field examinations, place the organisms in white plastic boxes.

- You may need to fix some specimens in 70 percent alcohol.

Data and Analysis

The graph in Figure 8 should show a decrease start-

Figure 3 data

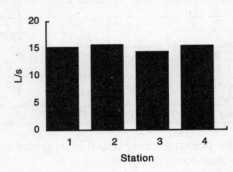

ing after sunrise and continuing throughout the light hours because CO_2 is used in photosynthesis.

The pH will not vary much along the entire stream because of the mixing of water. If inlet pipes or tributaries are present, their contents may change the pH.

1. The rapids; many insects are adapted to capture food as the water flows by. A larger volume of food passes through narrow channels. Some insects set up small "nets" to capture food. They also are adapted to moving about in fast-flowing water.

2. Most aquatic insects go from their immature stage to adult stage in the summer months. During early spring, the freshwater streams are overrun with aquatic insect larvae.

3. It depends on the type of algae. Attached algae will be abundant in fast-moving water. Floating mats will be abundant in pools.

4. Factors will vary with the species, but nutrient concentration, temperature around 13°–21°C, optimum sunlight, suitable substratum for attached algae and slow waters for mats of floating algae are some.

5. Students should explain answer by citing habitat preference of organisms.

6. Answers will vary. Structures for burrowing into silt, gills that move back and forth, mouth-parts

of insects which can capture and pierce prey are some adaptations of animals living in pools. Plants can be shallow-rooted and may contain stems and leaves lacking stomata. Animals living in rapids may have adaptations, such as claws for attachment (insects), a muscular foot (mollusks), or bodies and muscles adapted for orientation in the water (fish), mouth-parts for straining food, and body shape that lowers water resistance.

7. The volume of flow past any given point should be the same at all stations sampled. If the channel is narrow and shallow, the velocity of the stream will be faster. Velocity changes with width and depth of the stream.

8. The color and turbidity can prevent photosynthesis in plants attached to the bottom. Eggs laid on the bottom may be covered by silt and may not get enough oxygen.

9. The water temperature should remain nearly the same throughout the day, especially in fast-flowing water. The air temperature will show more variation.

10. An increase in intensity and duration of sunlight on water could cause changes. Slow-moving water absorbs more light than fast-moving water. Increase in turbidity can cause an increase in heat absorption.

11. It will decrease with an increase in light and photosynthetic activity.

12. An increase in photosynthetic activity results in an increase in the oxygen content. Oxygen also enters water when water ripples. pH can vary because of the carbon dioxide used in photosynthesis.

13. Some animals and plants cannot tolerate wide ranges of pH and an increase in carbon dioxide.

14. Rapids: Arthropoda (crustaceans and insects); deep pools: Chordata. Rapids provide "washing in" of material for small invertebrates. Deep pools provide shelter and food for large animals.

15. Answers will depend on streams. Rapids will have more attached plants, while pools have more emergent and floating plants.

LAB 17
Testing Water Quality
Objectives
- Measure the concentration of dissolved oxygen in water samples obtained from different locations using a dissolved oxygen probe.
- Give reasons why the water samples have different concentrations of dissolved oxygen.

Time Allotment
time outside of class to collect water samples
1 class period to conduct the lab

Materials
LabPro or CBL 2 unit (6)
AC adapter (optional) (6)
TI graphing calculator (6)
link cable (6)
Vernier dissolved oxygen probe (6)
sodium sulfite calibration solution (6 bottles, included with the probes)
D.O. electrode filling solution (KCl solutions) (6 bottles included with the probes)
Beral pipette (6)
dissolved oxygen calibration bottle (6, included with the probes)
metric ruler (6)
classroom thermometer
classroom barometer
water samples from different locations (at least 4 samples for each group)
jars with lids (24 or more)
plastic or rubber gloves (30 pairs)
graduated cylinder (100 mL) (6)
graduated cylinder (10 mL) (6)
beakers (100-mL) (5)
distilled water (600 mL)
wax pencil (6)
lab wipes (1 package)

Preparation
To make more sodium sulfite solution, see page T10.

Teaching the Lab
- Have students work in groups of five.
- When students are finished with the sodium sulfite solution, they should gently squeeze the bottle before closing it to remove air from the top of the bottle.

- Discuss with students the concepts behind the calibration procedure. Sodium sulfite removes dissolved oxygen from a solution. If the sodium sulfite solution has been stored brim-full in its bottle, you can assume it is oxygen-free. A second calibration point is the value of dissolved oxygen in air-saturated distilled water. These two points can set up a calibration line with a defined slope.
- The dissolved oxygen probe can be stored for several days with filling solution inside, as long as the membrane tip is submerged in water. If the probe is stored longer, the inside of the membrane cap must be rinsed and dried prior to storage.

Data and Analysis

Sample	Water Source	Observations of Water	Concentration of Dissolved Oxygen (ppm)
1	Tap	Clear	7.62
2	Aquarium	No water movement; stagnant	7.12
3	River	Murky; somewhat polluted	4.12
4	Puddle with algae	Green-colored	11.60

1. Answers will vary. Water that is flowing, being bubbled with air, or populated with photosynthetic organisms will have a high dissolved-oxygen concentration; stagnant, polluted, or very warm water will have low dissolved-oxygen concentrations.

2. (a) Samples with a dissolved oxygen concentration lower than 4 ppm could not support aquatic life.

   (b) Aquatic organisms are unable to get the oxygen they need from the air. The oxygen must be dissolved in the water in which they live.

3. Dissolved oxygen in the water comes primarily from aquatic organisms undergoing photosynthesis. The deeper the water, the less light is available for photosynthesis. Therefore, the concentration of dissolved oxygen decreases with water depth.

4. Students might say they did not warm up or calibrate the probe properly, did not swirl the samples with the probe, or had introduced air into the samples by shaking them.